A BOUQUET OF
WILD FLOWERS

Frontispiece

Cynthia Abbott.

A BOUQUET OF WILD FLOWERS

Painted by
HYACINTH ABBOTT

and described by
JOHN HUTCHINSON, LL.D., F.R.S., V.M.H.

BRUCE & GAWTHORN LTD.
Hunters Lane, Leavesden, Watford, Herts.

Introduction

Though they represent only a small fragment of the whole flora of the world, the wild flowers of our islands provide a fascinating study from several points of view, botany nowadays being a very broad subject. It is perhaps the most easily accessible of the natural sciences, flowers being found almost everywhere in the world except in regions permanently covered with ice and snow. They appeal to the wonder of children, and for a multitude of older people their cultivation provides an unrivalled hobby. To many, however, the study of botany appears to involve the learning of long Latin names, and still harder facts, at least at the outset. But it differs little from, and is much less difficult than, other sciences in this respect.

Flowering plants, some lovely examples of which are shown in this book, represent the peak or climax of evolution in the vegetable world, and there is a wonderful partnership between them and insects. Flowers supply insects with food in the form of nectar and pollen, whilst the insects, in turn, probing for the nectar, carry the pollen from flower to flower, resulting in the fertilization of the ovules that later develop into seeds.

Scattered over the whole world there are well over two hundred thousand *species* of flowering plants grouped into nearly fifteen thousand *genera*, the latter in turn being classified in upwards of three hundred more or less natural *families*. A *genus* usually consists of several to many species which are clearly related by some common character or characters, or it may contain only one species. *Families*, likewise, are made up of one to many genera of varying degrees of affinity. As there are many wild species of the genus *Rosa* scattered over the temperate parts of the world, millions of people know a Rose. *Rosa* is the hallmark (the standard or type genus) of the Rose Family, *Rosaceae*, and to it belong the Apple, Plum, Cherry, Blackberry, Raspberry, Strawberry, and many others, all with flowers which have a very similar structure in different degrees. Collectively they constitute the family *Rosaceae*.

Another family which may easily be recognized is the Daisy family, *Compositae*, so-called because the apparent flower is really a collection of several to numerous flowers (florets) arranged on a shortened axis and surrounded by bracts. Associated with the Daisy in the same family are such obviously related plants as Asters, Chrysanthemums, and Dahlias, and many others, and collectively they represent a very high stage in evolution in the world of flowers, as do likewise the Orchids and Grasses.

We cannot get very far with classification, however, if we confine our studies to our native British plants, for they represent only a fraction of the whole world flora. For every hundred wild species of plants only about one is found in Britain, and nearly all of them grow elsewhere in Europe.

In Britain we are hardly ever without wild flowers of some kind. Our winters, at least in the south and west, are usually mild enough for their growth, frosts being spasmodic and not often very prolonged. Even in late autumn or early winter in mild weather a few plants break prematurely into flower, as if a second spring had come. Such are the White and Purple Deadnettles, and *Euphorbia peplus* and *Stachys arvensis*, whilst about Christmas time the Christmas Rose, Snowdrop and Winter Aconite soon appear even when there is still snow on the ground, though none of the last three is truly native.

For most other wild flowers, however, there is a marked period of rest of several months, and they have various ways of surviving the winter. Trees, except the evergreens, lose their leaves, but most herbs disappear altogether. Perennial herbs have underground root-stocks and send up new shoots annually, annuals die down and bury their seeds in the soil, a new generation being produced each year.

A fascinating branch of botany is *Ecology*—the study of plants in relation to their environment, the chief factors of importance being water supply, climate and soil, and to a less extent in this country, elevation. For example many plants which are common on our chalky North and South Downs in southern England are rarely met with in other districts which have different surface soils. One would not look for them amongst the bracken and heather in the acid soil of the Bagshot Heath, only a little to the north, in the Lake District or the Scottish moors or in the deep rich soil of the Fen districts of East Anglia. A few plants typical of the principal habitats for wild flowers in Britain are noted in the following pages.

Woodland Plants

Woodland is mainly the habitat of spring flowers which bloom early whilst the trees are still leafless. There are summer flowers in woods as well, of course, but they grow mostly in the open spaces, where the trees do not entirely shut off the light and sun.

Beneath the Hazel-Nut bushes (*Corylus avellana*) (fig. 1), some of the more beautiful and conspicuous flowers of woodlands are Wood Anemone (*Anemone nemorosa*) (fig. 2), Primrose (*Primula vulgaris*) (fig. 3), Bluebell (*Scilla nonscripta*), and the Daffodil (*Narcissus pseudonarcissus*). The Snowdrop (*Galanthus nivalis*) the first plant to flower, is not considered to be truly native. The Lesser Celandine (*Ficaria verna*) (fig. 4) is too well known to need more than mention.

Other familiar plants in woods are the Common Bugle (*Ajuga reptans*), and the Foxglove (*Digitalis purpurea*), a highly poisonous, and, at the same time, medicinal plant. Plants with small inconspicuous flowers are Annual Dog's Mercury (*Mercurialis annua*), which belongs to the Spurge family, *Euphorbiaceae*, and the Enchanter's Nightshade (*Circaea lutetiana*). As mentioned on page 68 the beautiful Rose Bay (*Chamaenerion angustifolium*) often takes possession of a wood after it has been cleared of its trees, as it does of bombed sites in towns and cities.

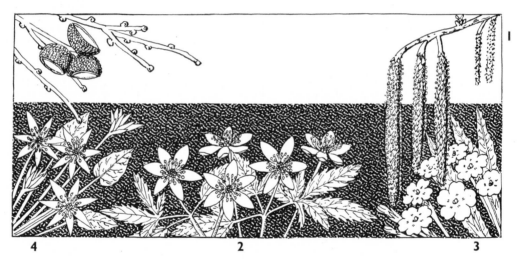

4   2   3

In some of the woodlands of Durham, Yorkshire, and Westmorland there was once found in some abundance our largest-flowered British orchid, the Lady's Slipper (*Cypripedium calceolus*), its leaves rather like those of Lily of the Valley, with a large slipper-like pouched yellow and spotted lip, the sepals and petals more or less purple, combining to make a most lovely flower. It is now seldom seen except in cultivation.

There are many other woodland plants of absorbing interest, but we have room to mention only one more, the Twayblade (*Listera ovata*), a weird member of the Orchid family, with a slender stem bearing a pair of large broad oval leaves, and above them a long spike of small yellowish-green flowers.

Flowers of the Hedgerows

Best known among the flowers of the hedgerows which divide fields and border country lanes, are in some places, especially near farms, the Nettles, both Stinging and Deadnettle. The Stinging Nettle (*Urtica dioica*) has very tiny flowers and is distantly related to the Hop and even the Elm. The stems are very fibrous and were at one time used for textile purposes. On the other hand the White and Purple Deadnettles (*Lamium album* and *Lamium purpureum*) do not sting and have showy white and purple flowers respectively.

7   6   5

A very conspicuous flower of the hedgerows is the Cuckoo Pint, Wild Arum, or Lords and Ladies (*Arum maculatum*). This is not just one flower but is a collection of numerous unisexual flowers enveloped in a hood-like spathe, from which emerges later on a spike of bright red very poisonous berries. In the Hawthorn hedge, itself a wild flower (*Crataegus*), there may be specimens of climbing Honeysuckle (*Lonicera periclymenum*) (fig. 5), Wild Roses (*Rosa canina*), and Woody Nightshade (*Solanum dulcamara*) (fig. 6), the latter also poisonous in all its parts, whilst in chalky districts the hedge may bear a mass of Traveller's Joy (*Clematis vitalba*). Growing in the shade of the hedge there will often be the lovely Herb Robert (*Geranium robertianum*), with small bright crimson flowers, Primroses (*Primula vulgaris*), and Dog's Tooth Violet (*Viola canina*).

Again in the hedge itself, especially in chalky districts, may be specimens of Dogwood (*Cornus sanguinea*), the Wayfaring Tree (*Viburnum lantana*), and the Guelder Rose (*Viburnum opulus*) (fig. 7), the last mentioned with an umbel of flowers like that of *Hydrangea*. In some districts the hedges are often festooned with both the White Bryony (*Bryonia dioica*), and the Black Bryony (*Tamus communis*), which belong to quite different families, the former with lobed leaves and tendrils, and yellowish green flowers, with red or orange berries, the latter with heart-shaped leaves, slender racemes of small flowers, and again with scarlet berries; both kinds very poisonous. Many other wild flowers find sanctuary in the hedgerows, as they do also by railway tracks.

Flowers of the Meadows

When we speak of wild flowers of the meadow, we bring to mind at once Buttercups (*Ranunculus*) (fig. 11) and Daisies (*Bellis*), which mingle so freely with the more dominant grasses. The greater number of meadow plants are perennials, growing up year after year from the same root-stocks, and amongst these annual plants have not much chance of existence. They thrive better in cultivated land such as cornfields.

Conspicuous before the hay is cut is the Ox-eye-Daisy, which is a *Chrysanthemum* (*C. leucanthemum*) (fig. 8), and related to those so named and grown in our gardens and greenhouses. Often here and there in a meadow are examples of another member of the Daisy family with lovely flower-heads of a delicate blue. This is Chicory (*Cichorium intybus*) (fig. 9), whose roots are dried, roasted and used for adulterating coffee. Another quite handsome member of the same family is the common Dandelion (*Taraxacum officinale*), which provides food for rabbits, whilst plants with even more nuisance value to the farmer are various kinds of Thistle (*Cirsium*). The common Daisy (*Bellis perennis*) flowers nearly all the year round, but closes its heads at night and during dull weather. Though it is capable of spreading rapidly, it possesses no pappus to assist in its distribution by the wind, as have most others of the same family (*Compositae*).

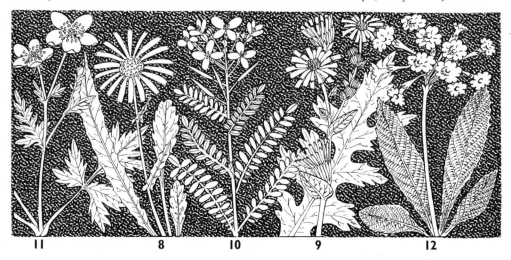

11   8   10   9   12

One of the most beautiful meadow-plants is the Meadow Geranium (*Geranium pratense*) (see page 102), which flowers just before the hay is cut, as also the lovely Cowslip (*Primula veris*) (fig. 12). Another most lovely and familiar spring flower is Lady's Smock (*Cardamine pratensis*) (fig. 10), which has several other names, such as Bittercress, Cuckoo-flower, and Milkmaid. The flowers are sometimes pure white but are more often tinged with lilac or pinkish purple.

Before leaving the meadow, with its numerous and lovely wild flowers, we must also mention the Clovers (*Trifolium*), which, with the grasses, make up the hay. These are the Red and White clovers, and they are also valuable bee plants. Related to them are other plants of the same family, *Papilionaceae*, the Wild Peas or Vetches, of which there are several kinds.

Flowers of the Cornfield

Several lovely wild flowers seem to thrive best in cultivated land, especially in cornfields. Chief among them are the Poppy, the Corn Marigold, Corn Cockle, Charlock, and Pheasant's Eye, and many others.

The Poppy (*Papaver rhóeas*) (fig. 13) often provides a wide expanse of scarlet in the landscape well before the corn is ripe. Its two sepals fall off on opening, leaving the four bright red petals to carry on the work of attracting insects to the plentiful store of pollen which they collect, for there are no nectaries.

The Corn Marigold (*Chrysanthemum segetum*) belongs to the Daisy family and is related to the *Chrysanthemum* of our greenhouses and herbaceous borders. Though such a beautiful plant, it is a troublesome weed to the farmer, for its seeds have the power of lying dormant in the soil for several years, coming to life when turned up by the plough. "Yellow Gowans," "Gowlans," "Gools," and Yellow Bottle are other names for it in different parts of the country.

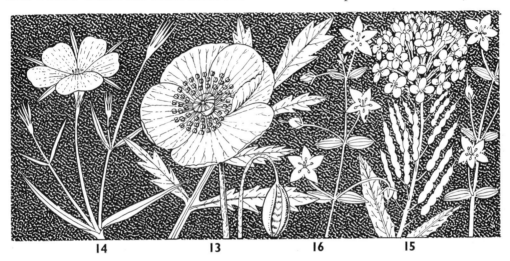

14   13   16   15

Corn Cockle (*Lychnis githago*) (fig. 14) flowers during July and August, and unlike the Pimpernel, its mauve blossoms remain open during the night and in bad weather. The seeds are covered with short tubercles which serve to fix it in the soil. They are poisonous and dangerous if mixed with cereals, giving a disagreeable odour to bread which renders it unfit for human consumption.

Charlock (*Sinapis arvensis*) (fig. 15) provides a yellow blaze in many cornfields. The lower flowers ripen their fruits before the upper ones have opened, so it is difficult to eradicate.

Nowadays, with forecasts of the weather several times daily by wireless, country people have little need to rely on plants to warn them of approaching rain or storms. In former times, however, there was no common flower which had gathered around it a larger amount of weather lore than the tiny Scarlet Pimpernel (*Anagallis arvensis*) (fig. 16). From its habit of closing its flowers about two o'clock in the afternoon, or on the approach of bad weather, it acquired the names "Shepherds' Clock," "Poor-man's Weather-glass," and "Shepherds' Weather-glass," besides another charming nickname "John-go-to-bed-at-noon."

Downland Plants

Most of the plants growing on the downs, especially those with chalky soils, as in the North and South Downs of south-eastern England, are perennials, some of which are not found in other parts of the country with different types of soil.

Several belong to the Daisy family (*Compositae*). One of the most handsome of these is the Greater Knapweed (*Centaurea scabiosa*) (fig. 17), the large flower-heads with their comb-like bracts and bright crimson flowers being very conspicuous.

There are also several small Thistles, unmistakable among them being the Stemless Thistle (*Cirsium acaule*), the prickly leaves of which lie flat on the surface to the exclusion of other plants and form a rosette for the solitary sessile deep mauve or crimson flower-head. Another conspicuous example of the same family is the Goat's-beard (*Tragopogon pratensis*) (fig. 18) or, as it is called by country folk, amongst several other names, "Jack-go-to-bed-at-noon," because of its propensity to close up its yellow flower-heads in the afternoon or during dull weather.

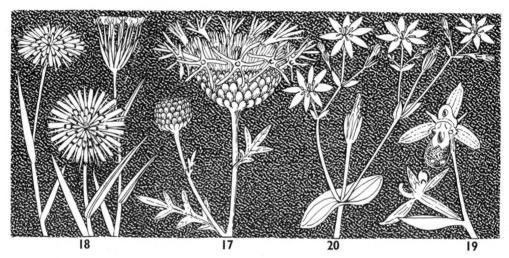

18   17   20   19

Other members of the Daisy family are the Mouse-ear Hawkweed (*Hieracium pilosella*), and the Yarrow or Milfoil (*Achillea millefolium*). It is here also that we meet with a "bank whereon the Wild Thyme grows" (*Thymus serpyllum*).

Other plants which are easily recognized are the Silver-weed (*Potentilla anserina*), with silvery-grey pinnate leaves and buttercup-like yellow flowers, whilst very pretty herbs are Lady's-fingers (*Anthyllis vulneraria*), and the Clustered Bell-flower (*Campanula glomerata*), growing here and there amongst the grasses which dominate the surface.

It is always a great thrill to find that gem of the chalk downs, the Bee Orchid (*Ophrys apifera*) (fig. 19), the lip of which bears a striking resemblance to the body of a female bee. Other delightful plants met with are members of the Gentian family, the Gentians themselves, with bluish flowers, and their relative the Yellow-wort (*Blackstonia perfoliata*) (fig. 20) with opposite entire leaves united around the stem (perfoliate), the eight corolla-lobes twisted anti-clockwise in bud.

Seaside Plants

Like other parts of the country, the seaside has its own particular flowers. Some of these are never found far from the shore, whilst others flourish also for some distance inland. Many of these maritime plants have thick fleshy leaves.

One of the most beautiful salt-marsh plants around Britain is the Sea Aster (*Aster tripolium*), often lining the gullies or forming pure stands, with erect grooved stems, narrow leaves, and beautiful mauve-blue ray flowers. Sometimes there are no ray flowers. Another lovely plant belonging to the same family, *Compositae*, is the Golden Samphire (*Inula crithmoides*) (fig. 21), a perennial herb with clumps of erect stems up to 1½ ft. high, succulent and shining. The leaves are broadly linear, often with two small teeth near the top. The flower-heads are about 1 in. diameter, the numerous rays rich cream-yellow, the disk flowers a darker hue. It is mainly found in the south and west, extending as far north as the south-west of Scotland, and also in south-east Eire. It is widely distributed in western Europe and in the countries around the Mediterranean.

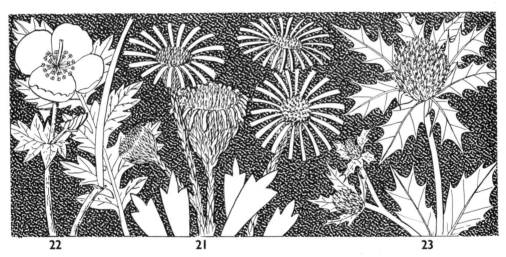

22 21 23

Sometimes quite common on sandy shores or amongst pebbles is the Yellow Horned Poppy (*Glaucium flavum*) (fig. 22), with thick deeply cut glaucous leaves, four yellow petals, and elongated slender fruits up to 1 ft. long and quite unlike those of the Cornfield Poppy. Another conspicuous plant in sandy places, often within reach of the sea spray, is the Sea Holly (*Eryngium maritimum*) (fig. 23), with prickly holly-like leaves surrounding heads of small lavender-blue flowers. This is a member of the Hemlock family (*Umbelliferae*), and not of the Daisy family (*Compositae*), which it mimics.

In damp sandy places and on rocks near the sea is often an abundance of Sea Thrift (*Armeria maritima*) with dense rosettes of small narrow needle-like leaves and a compact head on a long peduncle of small pink or, rarely, white flowers. Curiously enough this species is also found high up in some of the Cumberland and Scottish mountains. There are, of course, many other wild flowers which are adapted to life near the sea.

Flowers of Heaths, Moors and Mountains

Most conspicuous of the heath plants are, of course, the wide expanses of Ling or Heather (*Calluna vulgaris*), which needs no description, and the less common Bell Heather (*Erica cinerea*), and Crossleaved Heath (*Erica tetralix*) (fig. 24), all of which flower in the late summer and autumn and are a valuable source of honey.

Shrubs are represented by the lovely masses of Furze or Gorse (*Ulex europaeus*), about which Linnaeus enthused on his visit to England (see page 41), and by Broom (*Cytisus scoparius*), both members of the Pea family (*Papilionaceae*). Another less conspicuous member of the same family is the Needle Furze or Petty Whin (*Genista anglica*), a tiny shrublet with branches armed with long slightly curved sharp spines, these being the hardened leafless branchlets of the previous season.

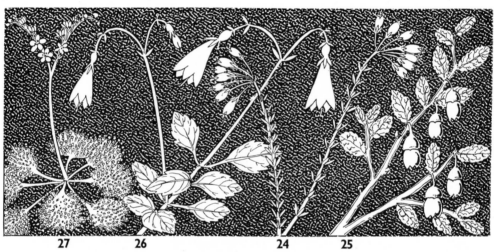

27   26   24   25

Another very common plant often associated with heather is the Bilberry, Blueberry or Whortleberry (*Vaccinium myrtillus*) (fig. 25), with flattened almost winged branches, deciduous oval leaves, and solitary pendulous flowers with globose corollas greenish and tinged with red. The blue berries are an important food for grouse and used locally for tarts and jam.

In Pinewoods in the mountains of northern England and central and eastern Scotland, but widely distributed in northern latitudes and in the mountains of southern Europe, is the much revered Twinflower (*Linnaea borealis*) (fig. 26). This genus is related to the Honeysuckle, and commemorates the name of the most famous naturalist of all time, that of Carl Linnaeus, of Sweden, known throughout the world as the "Father of Modern Botany." The Linnean Society of London (and of some other countries) serves to keep alive the memory of this remarkable man, and appropriately enough it was at a meeting of this society that Darwin read his famous paper on the origin of species.

In boggy places on the heath are often numerous plants of the Sundew (*Drosera rotundifolia*) (fig. 27), Britain's best example of an insectivorous plant, the sticky hairs on the rounded leaves attracting and imprisoning small flies.

Flowers of Ponds and Streams

The wild flowers of these habitats are either wholly aquatic or semiaquatic. The most showy of all is no doubt the White Water Lily (*Nymphaea alba*) (fig. 28), which flowers from June to September. Both the rounded leaf-blades and the handsome white flowers rest on the water. The latter are peculiar in that the sepals, petals and stamens grade into each other. A closely related plant is the Brandy Bottle or Yellow Water Lily (*Nuphar lutea*) (fig. 29), with very similar floating leaves but with yellow flowers elevated above the surface of the water. It has 12-15 small broad wedge-shaped petals quite different from the 5 green and yellow sepals.

Another very handsome aquatic or marsh plant is Yellow Flag (*Iris pseudacorus*), with sword-like leaves and large yellow flowers. A striking plant is the Arrow-head (*Sagittaria sagittifolia*) (fig. 30), with panicles of delicate white or pinkish flowers, the lower ones female without stamens, the upper with many stamens but no pistils. The leaf is arrow-shaped.

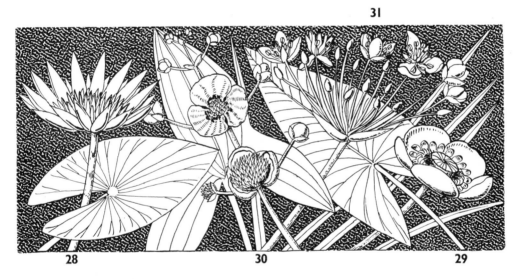

Less common is the so-called Flowering Rush (*Butomus umbellatus*) (fig. 31), with narrow strap-shaped leaves, a long flowering stem up to 4 ft. high, bearing at the top and high above the water an umbel of twenty to thirty pretty pink flowers. The anthers of these are remarkable, for before they open they are linear-oblong, but after releasing their pollen they shrink into a round ball.

There are many other aquatic or semi-aquatic plants with less spectacular flowers but which are of great biological interest. An example is the Bladderwort (*Utricularia vulgaris*), to be found in deep pools and canals, the leaves of which bear bladders that trap small aquatic animals whose decomposed bodies are sucked in by special absorption cells developed within the bladder. Its beautiful golden flowers are raised above the water on rather long stalks about midsummer.

Contents

CONTENTS

Crab Apple

Crab Apple

(MALUS PUMILA)

THE Crab is one of our most beautiful native trees, not only because of its lovely pink-tinted flowers in spring, but also later in the year with its attractive fruit (a favourite for making jelly), and the autumn colour of its leaves.

Crab Apple trees are found wild in hedgerows and woods from about the Forth of Clyde districts southwards, and in many parts of Eire, in some soils growing up to 45 ft. high or so.

During the daytime, Crab Apple flowers, like those of Honeysuckle, give off only a very slight smell of honey, but at night they exude an agreeable odour which attracts numerous night-flying insects. The lure to them is the nectar which is hidden inside the tube of the calyx, and whilst searching for it they become brushed with pollen, which they deposit on the stigmas of other flowers, thus bringing about cross-pollination. Fruit growers are now fully aware of the advantage of maintaining hives of bees in or near their orchards of apples, plums and pears. Self-pollinated flowers rarely set fruit.

Crab Apple flowers last from five to six days. The stamens are at first erect in the middle of the flower. Their unripe yellow anthers are either at the same level as the five already mature stigmas, or just below them. About two days after the bud has opened the anthers of the outer stamens begin to open, and afterwards those of the inner stamens. Meanwhile, the stamens diverge but little so that automatic self-pollination can readily take place. This may also occur when the flower fades, for at this stage the styles curve outwards to such an extent that the stigmas are brought into contact with the slightly diverging stamens.

Dog Rose

Dog Rose

(ROSA CANINA)

ROSES vie with the Honeysuckle in providing beauty and perfume to our hedgerows and woods. The most easily recognized of the many species and varieties of British roses are the *Dog Rose,* shown here, the *Sweet Briar* (Rosa rubiginosa), known by its unequal-sized prickles, deep rose-red flowers, and strongly scented foliage ; *Trailing Rose* (Rosa arvensis), a glabrous plant with few large unequal-sized hooked prickles, subglobose fruits, and large white odourless flowers; and the *Burnet Rose* (Rosa spinosissima), a very low growing prickly shrublet, with small leaves and large cream-coloured deliciously fragrant blooms.

Wild roses played an important part during the Second World War. For example, in the year 1943 no less than 500 tons of rose-hips were collected from the hedgerows and woods of Britain, mainly by children and members of the Women's Institutes. From these about $2\frac{1}{2}$ million bottles of National Rose Hip Syrup were prepared, roughly equivalent in Vitamin C content to 25 million oranges. Curiously enough it was discovered that wild roses in northern districts of Britain were richer than those farther south.

Besides this useful product, rose flowers provide food for insects which help to cross-pollinate them and other flowers, such as apples, pears and plums. In spite of the delicious fragrance of the Dog Rose, however, its flowers have no nectar, but they make up for its absence by producing a great amount of pollen which is collected and stored for food by visiting insects. Some other kinds of British roses do secrete nectar.

When the flower of the Dog Rose opens the stamens curve outwards towards the more or less erect petals, a visiting insect usually alighting on the stigmas in the middle, which are then dusted with pollen from another flower.

Blackberry, Bramble

HVA

Blackberry, Bramble

(RUBUS FRUTICOSUS)

B ESIDES its delicious fruit for making jam, jelly and puddings, the Blackberry serves a very useful purpose as a hedge-plant where it often combines with the Hawthorn and other shrubs to form a formidable barrier to stock. The long trailing stems are sometimes employed in country districts to bind the thatch on corn stacks.

Before ripening the berries are at first green, then bright red, and finally black, and all three conditions are often found on the same spray, giving a succession of ripe fruits over a considerable period towards the end of August and early September. Fortunately, the sepals are sharply reflexed below the fruit and not closely pressed to it as in the Strawberry, so that when ripe the fruit-portion is easily separated, just as in the Raspberry. The juicy parts of both the Bramble and Raspberry are the actual ripe fruits, i.e., the ripe carpels. The red juicy part of the Strawberry, however, is very different, for it is the enlarged *receptacle*, the actual fruits being the tiny brown pips dotted all over it.

The specific name refers to the woody or bushy nature of the plant, the Latin word *fruticosus* meaning full of shrubs or bushy. It does not allude to the fruit, the Latin word for which is *fructuosus*, abounding in fruit. This, indeed, would be an equally appropriate name.

The name Bramble originally meant anything thorny, and Chaucer applied it to the Dog Rose :—

> "He was chaste and no lectour,
>   And sweet as the Bramble flower
>   That bereth the red hepe."

The branches of the Blackberry grow in long sweeping curves and when the ends trail on the ground roots are often developed. The older part of the original branch then often dies, while the apex grows upwards and gives rise to a new plant. In the flower the outer anthers ripen first and turn their open faces upwards, insects effecting cross-pollination. Nectar is secreted by a fleshy ring on the receptacle below the stamens.

Marsh Cinquefoil

H.V.A.

Marsh Cinquefoil

(POTENTILLA PALUSTRIS)

AS the English name indicates this plant will be found in marshy places and spongy peat-bogs, especially in hilly districts, but away from chalky and limestone soils. It is very widely distributed around the north temperate zone, even in Greenland. In Scotland it ascends up to 3,000 ft. on Ben Lawers, to 1,700 ft. in Wales, and 1,500 ft. in Tipperary.

The creeping root-stock is blackish and was formerly used in tanning, and it also yields a yellow dye. The leaves, which are pinnately divided into two to three pairs of toothed leaflets, have a large broad stipule attached to them some distance from their base. The flowers are dark-purple-red, up to $1\frac{1}{2}$ in. in diameter, and few together in a terminal leafy cluster. The calyx is relatively big, but the petals are quite small and narrow, and there are 20-25 stamens with rounded, purple anthers.

The flowers are *protandrous*, that is to say, the stamens are mature before the stigmas. They secrete an abundance of nectar in a green ridge-like disk between the stamens and the carpels. The calyx is purple-red inside or almost brown, while the petals are rather brighter in colour. The stamens are in two whorls and at first erect, the inner anthers being above the carpels so that pollen must fall upon the stigmas. As these are still immature, however, self-pollination is not effective.

After the anthers have fallen off, the filaments bend back towards the perianth, leaving the space they occupied in the middle of the flower free for the styles. These, meanwhile, increase in length, and it follows that insect-visitors must effect cross-pollination. After fertilization the calyx closes up and exposes the undersurface.

7

Greater Salad Burnet

H.V.A.

Greater Salad Burnet

(SANGUISORBA OFFICINALIS)

GREATER SALAD BURNET grows in moist meadows mostly in northern Britain, but is rare in Eire. It belongs to the Rose family *(Rosaceae)*, of which it is a very highly evolved member.

It is a perennial herb with a black woody root-stock and annual stems up to about 2 ft. high. The pinnate leaves are mostly confined to the lower part of the stem, the upper part of the latter branching out into long-stalked rather lovely heads of dark-crimson or purple flowers. These flowers are all bisexual, i.e., each contains four stamens and a pistil with a single style, differing from the rather similar *Salad Burnet (Poterium sanguisorba)*, in which some of the greenish flowers are unisexual, i.e., the numerous stamens in one set of flowers, the pistil in another set, with two styles. There are no petals in either kind.

It is an interesting fact that many flowers, having dispensed with their petals, are collected into heads or clusters, which renders them more conspicuous to insect-visitors. If they remain inconspicuous then wind-pollination is adopted, as in the Poplars.

A peculiarity of the flower-head of the Greater Salad Burnet is that the flowers open in succession from below upwards, so that only a zone about one flower deep is in bloom at any one time. Insects effect cross-pollination, though self-pollination may also take place. They visit the flowers to collect the nectar secreted in a ring around the base of the style, and the four calyx-lobes act as nectar-receptacles.

This herb has been largely used in making Herb Beer, and was formerly in high repute as a vulnerary, hence its generic name, from *sanguis,* blood, and *sorbeo,* to staunch.

Broom

(CYTISUS SCOPARIUS)

NOWADAYS few of our wild plants are put to any use, the Broom being one of the exceptions. Broom-tops, both fresh and dried, are used in medicine as a slight stimulant for the kidneys, whilst the green angular flexible switch-like branches are employed in making baskets. When peeled they resemble cane.

Broom is found in nearly every county in Britain except in chalky soils. Turner, an early writer (1548) on British plants, made the following rather naïve remark about its distribution: " Broume groweth in al countriis of England where as I haue ben."

A characteristic of many plants of the Pea family, *Papilionaceae*, to which the Broom belongs, is that the roots bear small nodules containing bacteria which are capable of converting the nitrogen in the air into nitrates and used by the plant as food. Thus the soil is enriched by their presence, a fact well known to the farmer.

As in all other plants of this family, the flowers of the Broom are " irregular," with five free petals which are distinctly clawed, the upper one being the *standard* (vexillum), the two side petals the *wings* (alae), and the lower two petals form the *keel* (carina).

There is no nectar in Broom flowers, but humble- and honey-bees visit them for the sake of their pollen. This is discharged by an explosive mechanism which releases the stamens and style from within the petals where the pollen has been collected from the anthers. When an insect alights on the keel and wings, the weight of its body presses them down and the pollen is thrown on to the undersurface of the insect which carries it away and deposits it on the stigma of other flowers, thus effecting cross-pollination.

Broom

Red Clover

RED CLOVER is a valuable field crop and an important plant in permanent pastures and hay-fields. It is also valuable as a bee-flower, these insects effecting cross-pollination when searching for the abundant nectar at the base of each individual flower. Like most other kinds of clover, of which there are about 20 different species in Britain, it is a perennial plant, with handsome heads of reddish purple or rarely white flowers girt at the base by two sessile leaves.

The stipules of this clover are very conspicuous and about three-quarters of an inch in length, with sharply pointed lobes ; leaflets obovate, with numerous parallel nerves radiating into minute teeth on the margin. The calyx-lobes are very prominent and bristle-like when the flowers are in bud, purple, and one slightly longer than the others. It is worth while spreading out the petals under a hand-lens or dissecting microscope with a 15 or 10 magnifying lens, the back (dorsal) petal, the standard *(vexillum)* being shaped like a draining spade with a short handle (the *claw*), the wing-petals oblong and long-clawed, and the keel-petals very similar. Next come the stamens united into a sheath, except the upper one, which is free as in so many other members of the family *Papilionaceae*. And within the staminal sheath is the tiny ovary with its slender style and containing one ovule.

When a bee visits a head of clover-flowers to gather nectar, the weight of the insect presses down the wing and keel petals which release the stamens and pistil. When this happens the pollen is thrown on to the underside of the insect's head and is transferred to the stigma of another flower. The nectar is also stolen by other insects which perforate the flowers from the outside and thrust their proboscis through the hole. After flowering the petals turn brown, the calyx, remaining erect and enclosing the pod containing a single seed.

Red Clover

Spiny Rest-Harrow

(ONONIS SPINOSA)

THE Spiny Rest-Harrow is usually erect and shrubby, with a short root-stock and no creeping shoots. Usually the branches end in a sharp spine, and the pod is distinctly longer than the calyx. It grows by waysides and in barren fields and moors in England and Wales, but is rare in Scotland, and is not found in Eire. The flowers of this species are rose-red in colour with white wing-petals, more rarely all the petals pure white. There are no nectar guides and indeed no nectar.

There is a second and very similar species of this genus in Britain, which is more partial to limestone soil, and it is found in Eire. This is known simply as Rest-Harrow *(Ononis repens)*, and it derives its English name from the tough long subterranean shoots. It is an equally pretty plant with dark green foliage and bright rose-red flowers like those of a small Sweet Pea. Usually its branches have no spines, and the pod is distinctly shorter than the calyx.

Insect-visitors to the Spiny Rest-Harrow are mainly bees, which set in motion a pumping arrangement by which threads of pollen are thrown out on to the body of the insect. The 10 united filaments of the stamens are somewhat thickened just below the anthers, the five outer ones much more strongly than the others. The anthers of the five inner stamens, on the other hand, produce a larger quantity of pollen. Before the flower opens, the anthers extend to the base of the hollow formed by the tips of the keel-petals, completely fill this with pollen, and then shrivel up. At that time the stigma is situated a little below the apex of the keel. When the keel petals are slightly depressed by the insect, the thickened ends of the filaments are pushed farther into the pollen chamber, and a corresponding amount of pollen is squeezed out on to the body of the insect by which it is carried to the stigma of an older flower, thus effecting cross-pollination.

14

Spiny Rest-Harrow

Bird's-foot Trefoil

(LOTUS CORNICULATUS)

THIS is one of the most widely distributed species of the Pea family *(Papilionaceae)* in Britain. Hence it has a number of common names, such as Butter-jugs, Shoes and Stockings, Lady's Slipper, Cross-toes, Crow-toes, and in Yorkshire Cheesecake-grass. It is found on a great variety of soils, especially in chalk and limestone grassland, though it is usually absent from the richest soils.

It is a perennial herb with a very long tap-root by means of which it remains a close and verdant carpet in the meadows when other plants are dried up during long spells of drought. By clustering its lovely flowers together on a long common stalk, the species renders itself very conspicuous to insects, the back petal (the standard) being erect and often marked with red streaks which serve as nectar-guides to bees searching for nectar. The weight of the insect pressing on the wing- and keel-petals releases the pollen stored within their tips, whence it is transferred to the stigma of an older flower. Self-pollination is ineffective because the stigmatic portion of the style must be rubbed before it becomes receptive to the pollen.

Distinguishing features of the Bird's-foot Trefoil are its procumbent habit, leaves divided into three separate leaflets with a pair of large leaflet-like stipules at the base, the bright yellow flowers, and the inner cylindric pods which twist spirally when ripe and release the grey seeds mottled with dark brown. The uppermost of the 10 stamens is free from the remainder, which are united into an open sheath, as in most members of the Pea family.

Bird's-foot Trefoil

Tufted Vetcn

Tufted Vetch

(VICIA CRACCA)

SOME of the dozen or so British species of Vetch are highly organized tendril-climbers. One of the most handsome and showy is the Tufted Vetch *(Vicia cracca)*, which brightens up our hedges with its long racemes of numerous blue flowers borne to one side on a common stalk (peduncle). The leaves consist of about 10 pairs of narrow leaflets, the uppermost pair and the end leaflet being modified into a branched tendril by means of which it climbs over other plants.

Modifications in vegetative and floral structure for special purposes are very varied in flowering plants. For climbing, sometimes it is the leaflets, sometimes the leaf-stalk, which are modified, and in some the peduncle itself twists around the shoots of other plants.

Some parts of flowers are completely changed from their original function or they may fulfil a dual role, the modification usually compensating partially or wholly for the loss or reduction of other members. For example, the Wood Anemone has probably lost its petals, but the sepals have become coloured to keep up its attraction to insects. The Marsh Marigold and the Mezereon have the calyx similarly changed to a corolla-like structure. This subject of compensation or adaptation for the loss of parts of leaves, flowers or other organs in flowering plants provides a very interesting study, for there are many wonderful examples in plants which are not found wild in Britain.

The Tufted Vetch grows several feet high and is not likely to be confused with other species, except perhaps *Vicia orobus* and *Vicia sylvatica*, both of which resemble it in having the flowers on a longish common stalk, but they are not nearly so numerous and are much paler in colour, with broader leaflets.

Honeysuckle, Woodbine

Honeysuckle or Woodbine

(LONICERA PERICLYMENUM)

BRITAIN abounds in delightful country lanes and little woods, the air filled with the song of birds and the sweet scent of wild flowers. Maybe one side of the lane is overshadowed by a great hedge that has not known the billhook or shears for many a long year. Over the hawthorn and other small trees or bushes one is almost sure to find specimens of the lovely honeysuckle, a climbing plant needing support for its existence.

Climbing plants are divided into four groups: firstly those which twine spirally around a support, and are not aided by any other movement. Secondly, those endowed with irritable organs, which, when they touch an object, clasp it, such organs being modified leaves, branches, or flower-stalks. Plants of the third class ascend merely by the aid of hooks, and those of the fourth by rootlets. Honeysuckle falls into the first group.

The deliciously scented flowers of the honeysuckle open in succession only in the dusk of evening, when hawk-moths visit them and probe down the tube for the nectar at the bottom. In doing so they become dusted with the powdery pollen and transfer it to the stigma of an older flower, thus bringing about cross-pollination. This is more effective in producing fruits and fertile seeds than if they were self-pollinated. During the daytime the flowers are scarcely scented.

Though honey-bees sometimes visit these flowers, they have nothing to do with pollination, for they can only get at the nectar by boring a hole through the base of the corolla-tube. It seems likely, therefore, that the author of the well-known song, "The Honeysuckle and the Bee," was not much of a naturalist, or, if he was, took advantage of the licence allowed to song writers and poets.

Great Sallow Willow

Great Sallow Willow

(SALIX CAPREA)

UNLIKE some other kinds, the Great Sallow Willow is not used for weaving into baskets or the wood for making cricket-bats, but is employed for making fences and sheep-hurdles, which are more durable than those made of hazel. It is readily propagated by cuttings and from seed and is useful for planting to hold the soil on river banks. It grows naturally in woods, copses, and waste places, and in some plantations is so abundant as to become a forest weed. In Sussex it is used for making trug-baskets and rake-handles, as it is light and tough and splits easily.

Great Sallow Willow grows to a tall shrub or bushy tree up to 40 ft. high, sometimes with a trunk as much as a foot in diameter ; the winter-buds are fat, smooth, and ovoid, and the wrinkled leaves are ovate and broader in proportion to their length compared with most other British willows, and are cottony-hairy below. The stipules are large and leafy and soon fall off, and the male catkins are a little longer and thicker than the females, the latter being about two inches long in fruit, and both kinds very silky. As in most other willows, there are only two stamens in each of the male flowers which make up the male catkins, and there are no petals. The catkins are produced before the leaves unfold.

Heartsease

Heartsease

(VIOLA TRICOLOR)

ONE of the many pleasing features of this lovely violet is that it flowers from spring until the autumn. It is mostly found as a weed in cultivated ground, and is easily distinguished from other wild violets by its three-coloured petals, hence the species name, *tricolor*, and its deeply divided stipules. Being fairly common and widely distributed, there are several old English names for this favourite flower : " Kit-run-the-Street," " Love in Idleness," " Herb Trinity," and " Heartsease," the last mentioned from its supposed potency as a love charm.

In the Heartsease the lower petal is produced at the base into a spur in which nectar is secreted. The anther of each of the two lower stamens is provided with a nectar-secreting process which projects into the spur of the lower petal. An insect probing for the nectar touches the stigma and deposits on it pollen from another flower, thus effecting the more efficient cross-pollination.

In addition to the normal blossoms, some violets produce flowers which do not open and have only very rudimentary petals. These flowers are called *cleistogamous*, and they produce fertile seed.

Formerly, an older generation of botanists, such as the celebrated Kew pair, Bentham and Hooker, recognized only about six different native species of *Viola* in Britain. Some modern botanists, however, often less experienced, split them into about 26, a particularly striking example of divergent views in regard to species.

White Bryony

White Bryony

(BRYONIA DIOICA)

WHITE BRYONY has thick tuberous root-stocks which, in the past, have caused poisoning to those who have eaten them in mistake for turnips or parsnips. The red or orange berries are also poisonous. The stems are rather fleshy and trail over hedges and bushes by means of tendrils which arise by the side of the leaf-stalks. These tendrils are unbranched and spirally twist themselves around any other plant with which they come in contact.

The flowers of White Bryony are greenish white, about half an inch across, and bear either stamens or a pistil, but not both in the same flower or, indeed, on the same plant. In botanical language the flowers are *dioecious*, hence the name of the species, *dioica*. Those flowers with stamens are *male*, those with a pistil, *female*, the latter giving rise to the handsome red or orange berries in the autumn. The male flowers have five stamens, two pairs of the stamens being united together, the fifth separate, the anthers becoming wavy on opening. In the female flower there are no stamens, the ovary is below the calyx (ovary *inferior*), and the short style is three-lobed. In both sexes the petals are united into a short tube.

Several plants grow wild in England and Wales which are not found in Eire. White Bryony is an example, and it is also absent from Scotland. Others are the Black Bryony *(Tamus communis)*, Herb Paris *(Paris quadrifolia)*, the Snowdrop *(Galanthus nivalis)*, Lily of the Valley *(Convallaria majalis)*, Traveller's Joy *(Clematis vitalba)*, and a few others. Their absence is probably due to Eire having been separated from Great Britain before the latter was split off from continental Europe. Thus many species returned after the ice ages too late to cross over into Eire, and Eire, in consequence, has a poorer flora than Great Britain. On the other hand, Eire has some very interesting plants not found in Britain, such as the Strawberry Tree *(Arbutus unedo)*, found also in Spain and Portugal and the Mediterranean, and a few common also to North America.

Heather, Ling   Bell Heather   Cross-leaved Heath

(CALLUNA VULGARIS)   (ERICA CINEREA)   (ERICA TETRALIX)

THE common heather or ling is probably unique among plants in that it was actually the subject for a book by a layman (non-botanist) early in the present century. The book was compiled by one Alexander Wallace, Editor of the *Florists' Exchange,* New York, and entitled *Heather in Lore, Lyric and Lay.* Needless to say the author was a Scotsman who dedicated the work :

" To my loving wife, Rachel Marion, in grateful recognition of cheering encouragement and valuable assistance which lessened much of my present labours ; and of a constant devotion that has made separation from my native heather-land a happy exile."

On the title page he quotes :

> " Up amang the purple Heather,
> No' a flow'r that man can gather
> Frae garden fair
> Or greenhouse rare
> Can beat the bonnie bloomin' Heather."

Heather has entered into the literature, the poetry, the lyrics and into the home life of the Scottish people to a degree unsurpassed by any other plant in the history of nations. Scotland and heather are inseparable. It is essentially the dominant plant of the Highlands, where it grows in vast masses over wide areas, and it figures in many legends, being almost as national an emblem as the bagpipe.

In the past, heather furnished the Scot with much that was valuable in his daily life. It was, and still is, used for thatching houses and barns, making brooms, scrubbing-brushes and baskets, for weaving into fences, covering underground drains, and many other minor purposes. There would be little or no grouse-shooting without heather, and Burns said of it :

> " Moorcock springs
> On whirring wings
> Amid the blooming heather."

Three different sorts of " heather " are shown on our plate, that on the left, Scotch Heather or Ling, in the middle, Bell Heather, and on the right-hand side the Cross-leaved Heath.

Heather, Ling
(LEFT)

Bell Heather
(MIDDLE)

Cross-leaved Heath
(RIGHT)

Common Mallow

(MALVA SYLVESTRIS)

THREE species of *Malva* are native in these islands, *Malva sylvestris* being much the commonest, growing in dry places, especially near houses, but rare in Scotland and often near the sea-coast. It is recognized by its erect stem, five- to seven-lobed leaves, and hairless, flat and disk-like fruit covered with a strong network of veins ; seeds flattened with a V-shaped slit on one side. It flowers from about the middle of June.

The calyx is hairy and five-lobed, and immediately below the lobes are three additional bracteoles fringed with long hairs, resembling an additional calyx (epicalyx). The usual position for bracteoles in flowers of other families is on the flower-stalk itself, but evolution has carried them up below the calyx in many *Malvaceae*, the family to which *Malva* belongs, and from which it gets its name.

The pale reddish-purple or blue petals are marked with darker circles which serve as nectar-guides, the nectar being protected by a bunch of hairs on each side near the base. At first the anthers are crowded together in the middle of the flower, completely covering the still immature stigmas. After the anthers have opened and released their pollen, their stalks (filaments) curve outwards and downwards and their place is taken by the stigmas which become receptive to pollen brought by insects from another flower.

The other two species of *Malva* found wild in Britain are the Dwarf Mallow *(Malva neglecta)*, a procumbent annual of roadsides and waste places, with much smaller flowers in axillary clusters and rounded, only very slightly lobed, leaves ; the second species is the Musk Mallow *(Malva moschata),* a perennial plant with very deeply divided leaves and rose-coloured or rarely pure white petals.

Spotting features of the *Malva* family are that the calyx-lobes do not overlap in the bud (they are always *valvate*), and the numerous stamens are united into a column around the style-branches. The anthers in the family have only one loculus or cell, due to the splitting of the filaments.

Common Mallow

Lady's Bedstraw

(GALIUM VERUM)

THIS lovely plant, with its myriads of tiny yellow flowers is a conspicuous object between June and September in many kinds of soils, such as sand, loam, or chalk. The flowers smell strongly of cumarin and are beautifully arranged in little cymes, the whole forming an oblong mass of blossoms, each little cluster having a whorl of small leafy bracts. Cross-pollination is brought about mainly by the feet of small insects crawling about among them and attracted by the scent.

The root-stock of this species is woody, short and creeping, the slender stems being covered with minute reflexed hairs which enable them to maintain their upright position amongst other herbage. The foliage is deceptive, however, though it looks innocent enough. For half the " leaves " are not really true leaves, but are leaf-like *stipules* which perform a similar function. They are in whorls of six or eight and the true leaves may be detected only if they have a tiny bud in their axils. This similarity of the leaves and stipules is a feature of most of the genera of the particular tribe *(Galieae)* of *Rubiaceae*, to which *Galium* belongs. *Rubia*, from which the family name is derived, is a related genus, and to the same family belong such important commodities as *Quinine* (from *Cinchona*, native of South America), and other drugs, and *Coffee (Coffea)*, from Arabia and tropical East Africa.

Lady's Bedstraw is sometimes a troublesome weed in pastures, but may be reduced by continual cutting in order to exhaust the root-stocks and prevent seeding. The fruits, which appear later, are quite smooth and rounded, and do not stick on the fur of animals like those of another species, the *Cleavers* or *Goosegrass (Galium aparine)*.

Lady's Bedstraw

Marsh Marigold

(CALTHA PALUSTRIS)

THIS lovely golden flower grows by the sides of brooks and streams, often with its roots in the water. A celebrated namesake of the present writer, A. S. M. Hutchinson, produced a best seller entitled *If Winter Comes,* and went on to say, "then spring must be behind." The Marsh Marigold, together with a few other plants, always proves this to be a truism, for it is a sure sign that winter, however long and dreary it may have been, has at last departed.

Though bearing a great resemblance to them, the Marsh Marigold is not a real buttercup, because there are no petals, the sepals having become coloured to make up for their absence, as in the Wood Anemone *(Anemone nemorosa).* The sepals are thus called upon to fulfil a dual role ; they protect the flower in the bud-stage and they attract insects to visit the flower for the nectar which is secreted at the base of the green carpels in the middle. In true buttercups *(Ranunculus)* the nectar is hidden in a small cavity at the base of the petals.

As it is always one of the first spring flowers to bloom, the praises of the Marsh Marigold have been sung by many poets, its bright golden colour rendering it a favourite everywhere. John Dryden wrote of it :—

"And get soft hyacinths with iron blue
To shade Marsh Marigolds of shining hue."

The generic name is derived from the Greek *kalathos,* a cup or goblet, to which the open flower may be likened. Although very beautiful it is more or less poisonous, especially at the time of flowering. Horses and cattle have died through eating it, but generally they avoid it.

Marsh Marigold

Greater Spearwort

Greater Spearwort

(RANUNCULUS LINGUA)

FLOWER-LOVERS in many countries can share the beauty of this lovely species of Buttercup, whose rich cream-yellow flowers spread out to quite 2 in. diameter. For it ranges right from Eire in the west as far as Siberia in the east, and south to the Himalayas. In the British Isles it grows as far north as Caithness.

This is the largest of our British Buttercups, and belongs to a section of *Ranunculus* characterized by long lance-shaped leaves set on smooth hollow stems, the latter a feature common to many plants which grow in marshy places. Botanists who study the family tree of flowering plants claim that this section of the Buttercup genus is not far removed from the *Alisma* family, *Alismataceae*, and that they represent primitive groups of Dicotyledons and Monocotyledons respectively. The flowers in both families have completely free and numerous carpels, considered to be an ancient feature, compared with the single ovary made up of united carpels characteristic of more advanced or highly evolved families such as, for example, the Poppy family (*Papaveraceae*).

The flower-buds of the Great Spearwort are very distinctive, the rounded pouched sepals giving a lobed or angular appearance, with here and there the tip of a petal emerging from the tight flower-pack. In the bud stage the wonderful gloss on the upper side of the petals, so attractive to insects later, is scarcely noticeable. The stigmas are receptive before the anthers have opened, cross-pollination being effected by flies, which usually alight on the stigmas, dusting them with pollen from another flower.

Lesser Celandine

Lesser Celandine

(FICARIA VERNA)

WHEN this lovely early spring plant produces a lengthy shoot, which it sometimes does when growing in dense shade, it will be observed that the leaves are *opposite*. This is very unusual in the Buttercup family *(Ranunculaceae)*, the only other exception being Traveller's Joy *(Clematis vitalba)*. This one character would therefore be sufficient to distinguish it from the true Buttercups *(Ranunculus)*, whose stem-leaves are *alternate*. But there are other characters. The pairs of leaves of the Celandine will also be found to be unequal-sized, for which the rather formidable term *anisophyllous* is employed by botanists. In addition, there are only three sepals and more than five petals, a combination of characters which does not occur in true Buttercups, and to crown all there is only one seed-leaf (as in Monocotyledons) instead of two.

The short perennial root-stock bears numerous finger-like tubers in addition to ordinary fibrous roots, and there are frequently small rounded bulbils in the axils of the leaves, especially on plants growing in very shady places.

The Lesser Celandine is one of the first flowers to open in early spring, and in consequence is known to most country children, who often test their liking for butter by the amount of reflection from the bright shining petals on the skin below the chin. These petals have a duller deeply coloured nectar-secreting base, and they often bleach with age. The carpels are not receptive to pollen until the anthers have opened, thus avoiding self-pollination.

When classed with the Buttercups the name for this plant is *Ranunculus ficaria*, under which name it will be found in most botanical books on the British flora.

Poppy

H.V.A.

Poppy

(PAPAVER RHOEAS)

IT is an old and oft-told story that when the great Swedish naturalist, Carl Linnaeus, visited Britain in late spring he fell on his knees and shed tears at the sight of Gorse in flower on a common. If he had come later in the year he would no doubt have done the same over a mass of Poppies, which are even more lovely spread out over a field of ripening corn. Needless to say, Poppies are not much appreciated by the average farmer, who regards them as a troublesome weed. Unlike the Buttercup, poppy flowers have no nectar, but insects visit them to feed on the pollen in the numerous stamens.

The scientific name of a genus of hymenopterous insects (bees) is *Megachile*. These are leaf-cutters. It is a large genus of world-wide distribution, containing many species of varied habits. All furnish their cells with bits of leaves and petals cut from trees and herbs, which they stick together and roll into cases to form their larval cells in the trunks of dead trees and old rotting palings.

From the bright-coloured petals of the Poppy one of these ingenious little insects, known as the Drapery Bee *(Megachile papaveris)*, chooses the hangings of her apartment. She dexterously cuts out the petals of the half-expanded flowers, and fits them for her purpose, overhanging the walls of her cell with this splendid tapestry, in which, when complete, she deposits her honey.

The structural characters of the Poppy flower to be noted are the reduction to only two sepals, which fall off on opening, the four petals, the outer of which are broader than long, the inner about as long as broad, the eight to twelve stigmatic rays not extending quite to the edge of the disk-like top of the ovary, and the little holes below the top of the capsule by which the tiny seeds escape.

Cuckoo Flower, Lady's Smock, May Flower

Cuckoo Flower, Lady's Smock, May Flower

(CARDAMINE PRATENSIS)

SHAKESPEARE mentioned quite a number of flowers in his plays. Of this lovely plant he wrote :

> " When daisies pied, and violets blue,
> And Lady-smocks all silver white,
> And Cuckoo-buds of yellow hue,
> Do paint the meadows with delight."

But the Cuckoo-buds in this verse were the buds of the Marsh Marigold *(Caltha palustris)*, shown on page 35.

Syme, the author of several classical volumes of British Wild Flowers, said of it, " Of its early appearance with the cuckoo as the harbinger of bright days and cloudless skies, we are appropriately reminded in calling it the Cuckoo Flower."

The Cuckoo Flower is a common and well-known perennial plant of damp, low-lying meadows and pastures, where its lilac flowers may be found from April until early June. Its presence in such places indicates the need of better drainage, which with liming and grazing will diminish it considerably.

In extra damp seasons the stem frequently bears small bulbils at the base of and sometimes on the leaves by which the plant may be vegetatively reproduced. This is a constant feature of another equally beautiful species, *Cardamine bulbifera*, which grows in some woods. Such bulbils are found chiefly in plants which, from lack of sufficient fertilization by insects or other cause, fail to produce a proper quantity of mature and perfect seed. Occasionally, flowers will be found in which the stamens and pistil are transformed into small flower-buds.

Formerly the flowers of the Cuckoo Flower were reputed to possess valuable medicinal properties and were used in cases of hysteria and epilepsy. The flowers were toasted on pewter dishes over a fire, the powder being then boiled in bottles covered and stopped with leather.

Wild Radish

Wild Radish

(RAPHANUS RAPHANISTRUM)

WILD RADISH is a common and troublesome annual or biennial weed of cultivation and of waste places, where it flowers freely from summer until well into the autumn. It is also called White Charlock and Runch, for the petals may be white with coloured veins or pale yellow, besides the more typical lilac colour as shown in the picture opposite. In northern Scotland and in the Hebrides the yellow-flowered variety, var. *aureus*, is more commonly found.

The Latin name is adapted from the Greek *raphanos*, which means quickly appearing, in allusion to the rapid germination of the seeds. It is readily recognized when in fruit. These have a long beak at the top, and below they are contracted between the four to seven seeds, or they may have only one or two seeds and are then not contracted. When they are contracted the fruits are described as *torulose*. The seeds are rounded and covered by a fine network.

The leaves are deeply pinnately lobed, the terminal lobe much the largest and rounded, often with darker-tipped teeth and clothed like the stems with bristly hairs. The flowers are rather large and showy, the petals being broadly spoon-shaped and either white with coloured veins, or pale yellow, or lilac as shown in the drawing.

In the flower there are four nectaries, two on the inner side of the short stamens, the other two between the long stamens. Automatic self-pollination takes place.

Charlock, Wild Mustard

(SINAPIS ARVENSIS)

A CORNFIELD full of Charlock may be a lovely sight to the traveller, but it is a nuisance to the farmer. It therefore rivals the Poppy from both points of view.

Charlock is a coarse-growing annual weed up to about two feet high. The stems are more or less prickly with stiff whitish hairs, and these hairs are also found mainly on the nerves of the coarsely toothed but otherwise undivided leaves. The flowers are yellow and very showy, at first collected in a congested raceme which soon elongates as the fruits develop. Some of the fruits are already nearly ripe by the time the uppermost flowers have opened.

The sepals spread horizontally, but soon fall off altogether and expose the nectar secreted between the bases of the filaments. The petals are spoon-shaped, with a slender claw-like lower part. The anthers are rather large and arrow-shaped (sagittate) at the base.

The fruits of Charlock are very distinctive, the upper part being composed of a stout beak, and the lower part, which contains the 10 to 12 black finely pitted-reticulate seeds.

The genera of *Cruciferae*, commonly known as the Wallflower family, are largely classified by the shape and structure of their fruits and seeds, the flowers being much of the same pattern throughout— four free sepals, four free petals, six stamens, four of them longer and two shorter, and a single pistil composed of two united carpels divided by a false septum, with the ovules inserted on the margins.

Charlock, Wild Mustard

Penny Cress

(THLASPI ARVENSE)

THE most striking feature about the Penny Cress is, of course, the fruit. They are more or less rounded like a coin, hence the common name, and they are flattened contrary to the thin partition which divides the fruit into two compartments. The actual size of the fruit, including the broad marginal wing, scarcely equals the size of a farthing, and the wing is deeply notched at the top. In each of the compartments of the fruit there are five or six seeds, which are dark brown, more or less horseshoe-shaped, and with several ribs following the general contour of the seed.

Penny Cress is an erect hairless annual up to about 15 in. high, ending in a raceme of very small white flowers, the lower flowers very quickly developing into fruit whilst the uppermost flowers are still in bud. As may be seen in the illustration, the stem-leaves have no stalks and are arrow-shaped (auriculate) at the base. If the minute flowers be dissected under a lens they will be found to consist of four tiny sepals, four slightly larger spoon-shaped petals, and six stamens, of which four are longer and two a little shorter, as in most members of the family *Cruciferae*, the Wallflower being a typical example.

The plant grows as a weed in cultivated fields and waste places and is generally distributed in Britain, flowering in summer and autumn. Another common name, mostly now forgotten, is *Mithridate Mustard*, from its former use in sauces. When chewed it has the odour and flavour of garlic. It was so-called from Mithridates VI, king of Pontus, who died about 63 B.C., and who was said to have rendered himself proof against poisons by the constant use of antidotes. The scientific name *Thlaspi* is from the Greek *thlaein*, to crush, from the flattened fruit.

Penny Cress

Cheddar Pink

(DIANTHUS GRATIANOPOLITANUS)

THIS lovely Pink is found in and near the Cheddar Gorge in Somerset, where it grows in considerable quantity on limestone rocks and flowers during June and July. It occurs nowhere else in Britain, except in cultivation, but is otherwise widely distributed in west, central and southern Europe. This is a very interesting example of what is termed by naturalists "discontinuous distribution."

It is unfortunate that so beautiful a plant should be saddled with such a long specific name, which, however, must be used according to international rules in preference to the name under which it is described in older botanical books, namely *Dianthus caesius*.

The Cheddar Pink has a loose tuft of spreading green leaves at the base of each stem, the latter bearing only three or four pairs of opposite narrow leaves. These stem-leaves are three-nerved, the two lateral nerves very close to the margin. The flowers are deep pink and are scented. Below each flower are four bracts, the innermost pair being half to three-quarters as long as the calyx. The calyx is tubular, shortly five-lobed, with numerous parallel nerves, the lobes triangular. The petals have a jagged margin and there are 10 stamens, whilst the long ovary in the middle is shortly stalked (stipitate) at the base, with two separate styles. The fruit is a capsule which opens by four valves at the top.

The two styles, when the flower opens, will be found to be twisted together within the tube formed by the stalks of the petals. The five outer stamens shed their pollen first, then the other five, and after that the styles elongate and their stigma-bearing ends project from the flower, filling its entrance and are then ready to receive the pollen carried by an insect from other flowers.

Cheddar Pink

Ragged Robin

(LYCHNIS FLOS-CUCULI)

OTHER names are Rose of Heaven, Smooth Lychnis, Meadow Pink, and Wild Williams. It is one of the most easily recognized plants in the British flora because of its distinctive petals, which are deeply cut into four linear lobes, whilst the claw has two little lobes or appendages near the middle.

This plant is a perennial with rather weak stems and long internodes between the pairs of opposite narrow leaves, which are fringed with hairs towards the base. The flowers appear in late spring and early summer and are loosely clustered in terminal cymes, the oldest flower always in the middle and often well developed into fruit whilst the others are still in bud. The calyx is five-lobed and marked with 10 conspicuous ribs. The outer five of the 10 stamens mature first and their anthers, as they open, occupy the middle of the flower, soon curving outwards to make room for the inner five, which release their pollen in turn. Then the five styles develop and occupy the same position in the middle of the flower and become receptive to pollen carried from other flowers by insects which visit them for the nectar secreted at the base of the stamens.

The fruit of Ragged Robin is a capsule, opening at the top by five teeth, the styles often remaining. The numerous seeds are attached by little stalks to the central axis and are kidney-shaped and very closely warted. If a section be cut with a razor blade, it will reveal the beautiful little plantlet (embryo) curved around the endosperm, a characteristic of the family *Caryophyllaceae,* to which Ragged Robin belongs.

Ragged Robin

Soapwort

Soapwort

(SAPONARIA OFFICINALIS)

OTHER common names for this plant are Bruisewort, Fullers'
Herb and Bouncing Bett. When boiled or bruised in water the
leaves become saponaceous, and were formerly used as a substitute
for soap. The lather so formed has all the effects of soap and readily
removes grease. The scientific name was given because of this
quality, from the Latin *sapo*, soap. Saponin is a substance which
has a harmful effect on the blood and causes purging and vomiting
in animals.

Soapwort is found chiefly in the south-west of England and in
Wales, and frequents hedges, roadsides and fields. It is a perennial
with several rather stout leafy stems up to about 2 ft. high. The
opposite ovate-lanceolate leaves are connected at the base by a marked
rim across the stem, and they gradually merge into bracts in the upper
parts of the plant, being strongly marked with three to five nerves
parallel with the margins. The flowers are large and handsome and
arranged in a series of small cymes with a pair of narrow bracts below
each flower. The five petals are free from each other and pale pink,
lilac, or nearly white, with a long claw and a broad blade notched at
the top, the claw furnished with a two-toothed scale on the inside.
The 10 stamens are well exserted from the petals, and on top of the
ovary are two separate slender styles. The fruit is a capsule which
opens at the top by four small teeth releasing the seeds.

The fragrant odour of the flowers becomes much stronger in
the evening, and both day- and night-flying hawkmoths are the chief
visitors which collect the nectar secreted at the bottom of the calyx-
tube. Double flowers sometimes occur, especially when grown in a
garden. It flowers in summer.

H.V.A.

Yellow Loosestrife

Yellow Loosestrife

(LYSIMACHIA VULGARIS)

THOSE who may know little about the families of flowering plants might well ask why this lovely flower should be classified with the Primrose and the Cyclamen in the same family, *Primulaceae*.

The main reason is, of course, that the floral structure of all of them is much on the same pattern. The petals are united into a tube; the stamens are the same number as the corolla-lobes (united petals), and are inserted *opposite* to them in the tube. And if a cross-section of the ovary of any one of them be cut with a razor-blade, it will be found that there is only one compartment (loculus), with the numerous ovules arranged on a free basal placenta falling short of the top of the ovary. These, then, are the fundamental characters of the Primrose family, *Primulaceae*.

Yellow Loosestrife is a perennial plant with erect stems up to about 3 ft. high, growing on shady banks near water. The lower leaves are in whorls of three or four, the upper mostly in pairs, the margins minutely jagged. The five sepals are fringed with short hairs and the corolla-lobes are twisted (contorted) in bud and densely covered above by short glandular hairs which are also found on the stalks of the stamens. There are five of the latter with as many rudiments of stamens between them, which is an indication that the ancestral forms of this plant had probably *ten* stamens, pointing back to the more primitive family *Caryophyllaceae*.

Although there are no nectaries in the flowers to attract insects, there is an abundance of pollen in the relatively large anthers which is collected by certain bees and carried in balls on their hind-legs from one flower to another.

Marsh Gentian

Marsh Gentian

(GENTIANA PNEUMONANTHE)

THE Marsh Gentian is the tallest and has the largest flowers of our native species. It is locally frequent in moist places on heaths, but is absent from Scotland and Eire. It is well worth a place in a garden.

It reappears year after year, being a perennial with thick spreading roots and stiff stems up to about 2 ft. high. The leaves are opposite, as in all Gentians, sessile, lanceolate to linear, the broader with three distinct parallel nerves. There are several flowers to each stem, the middle one being the oldest and soon withering brown whilst the others are still in bud ; calyx with two leafy bracts at the base, its five lobes narrow and widely separated from each other and equal-sized. The corolla is beautifully varied in colour, tinged with green outside and the lobes a beautiful deep blue, mottled with green and white spots inside the tube ; each of the five corolla-lobes has a short triangular lobe between. The five stamens are inserted near the base of the corolla, and their anthers are connivent into a cone around the style and face outwards.

Nectar is secreted at the base of the narrow stipitate ovary and is protected from rain by the closing of the corolla during dull weather and at night. Humble-bees effect cross-pollination, and they are guided to the nectar by small whitish circles with brownish centres from which alternating blue and whitish lines point to the base of the flower. The bees creep half-way down the corolla-tube and are then able to reach the nectar protected by the filaments, at the same time becoming dusted with pollen from the cone of anthers.

Water Violet

Water Violet

(HOTTONIA PALUSTRIS)

WATER VIOLET is one of the most lovely of our aquatic wild flowers, and it is indeed a sight for tired eyes to behold a ditch or backwater filled with it in full bloom. It may be seen at its best in late May and early June at many places in Oxfordshire, where it is particularly abundant.

There are two types of flower, just as in the Primrose. One set of flowers have long styles and short stamens, the latter concealed within the corrolla-tube, another set have short styles with long stamens protruding some distance from the tube. Insect visitors, when searching for the nectar secreted at the base of the ovary, touch the anthers of the short stamens and become dusted with pollen which they deposit on the stigma of a short-styled flower. The reverse process happens to the other kind of flower, the pollen from the long stamens being deposited on the stigma of a long-styled flower.

Christian Konrad Sprengel, a German botanist, was the first to discover this condition (known as heterostyly) in the Water Violet, but he was unaware of its significance for ensuring more effective cross-pollination.

The Water Violet is not at all related to true Violets (*Viola*) but is so-called because it floats in water with its long trailing root-stock generally embedded in mud. The branches at the base of the main flower-stalk are arranged in a whorl and below them are the deeply divided leaves set out in a similar way. After fruits are formed the branches separate from the parent plant and form the starting points for new plants in the springtime, when they may be found floating about, often without roots, which develop later on. The seeds when ripe sink to the bottom within a week.

Hottonia was named in honour of Peter Hotton, a Dutch botanist, author of some books on medicinal plants.

Sea Thrift

Sea Thrift

(ARMERIA MARITIMA)

THIS lovely plant, so common in salt marshes and on rocky ledges near the sea, also grows high up in mountainous districts far from the sea in Cumberland and Scotland. Very few other British maritime plants show this peculiar distribution.

The flowers smell of *Cumarin* or *Coumarin,* a vegetable proximate principle ($C_9H_6O_2$) obtained from the Tonka Bean *(Dipteryx odorata),* and also occurring in Melilot and some other plants, to which it gives flavour to the Swiss cheese called *schabzieger.*

The plant is a tufted perennial with densely crowded narrow grass-like leaves, and simple leafless flowering stems covered with short soft hairs, and bearing at the top a rounded head of usually pink, more rarely white, flowers, surrounded by an involucre of bracts. The outermost of these are longer than the others and elongated at the base to form a reflexed sheath around the peduncle. The calyx-teeth are very short and narrow and united into a membranous tube, and each of the five free petals has a stamen inserted opposite to its base. The tiny ovary has only one compartment, with a single pendulous ovule, and it is topped by five free styles covered with spreading rod-like hairs at the base. These hairs form a dense felt which effectively protects the nectar concealed at the top of the ovary.

The erect stamens open as soon as the flowers do, so that insects probing for the nectar dust themselves with pollen and may effect either cross- or self-pollination. Towards the end of flowering, the styles and stamens become closely intermingled, ensuring self-pollination.

Purple Loosestrife

(LYTHRUM SALICARIA)

SOME plants look almost as beautiful when reflected in still water. The Purple Loosestrife is one of these, for its habitat is by ditches, ponds and rivers, where it makes a beautiful sight when it flowers in the summer. Being a perennial it reappears in the same spot year after year, its erect stems up to 3 ft. high; rather densely leafy, the leaves opposite in pairs or three in a whorl (verticillate), sessile and clasping the stem, lanceolate and gradually acute at the apex, the lateral nerves prominently looped. The flowers are arranged in a dense terminal spike-like raceme leafy towards the base, with smaller green leafy bracts throughout. The petals are reddish-purple or pink with darker veins.

The stamens in the Purple Loosestrife are about twice as many as the petals, and the structure and function of the flowers were very thoroughly investigated by Darwin. They are of three forms (trimorphic), differing in the comparative length of the stamens and styles, this arrangement being of benefit to the species. Some of the flowers have *long* styles, some *medium* styles and others *short* styles. In those with long styles half of the stamens are of *medium* length, half are *short*; in those with medium styles, half of the stamens are *longer* than the style, half are *short*; in those with short styles, half of the stamens are *long* and half of *medium* length.

Darwin showed that there are 18 possible modes of pollination in this arrangement, but that only six lead to complete fertility, in which each different length of style bearing the stigma receives pollen from anthers situated at a corresponding level, as in the Primrose. Insects visiting the flowers carry the pollen when searching for the nectar secreted in the fleshy base of the calyx.[1]

---

[1] This interesting device for cross-pollination is more fully described and illustrated by the author in his *British Wild Flowers*, Fig. 410 (Penguin Books Ltd., 1955).

Purple Loosestrife

Buckbean

(MENYANTHES TRIFOLIATA)

THE Buckbean is one of the most distinctive and lovely of our wild flowers. It grows in water, with creeping or floating rhizomes forming a thick mass from which arise numerous trifoliolate leaves and upright racemes of beautiful white flowers tinged with pink on the outside. The corolla-lobes are provided on the inside with dense white woolly hairs.

The flowers of the Buckbean are mostly of two kinds, some with longer styles and some with shorter styles, with a corresponding different position for the anthers on the corolla-tube. In this feature they resemble the common Primrose. In the long-styled form the anthers are lower in the tube, and in the short-styled form higher in the tube. Insects visiting the flowers, therefore, carry the pollen from the higher stamens to the stigma of the long-style and *vice versa*. This ensures cross-pollination which favours a better set of seed.

The Buckbean is usually classed with the Gentians in the family *Gentianaceae*, but by some botanists it is considered to represent a separate family, *Menyanthaceae*, together with the Fringed Water-lily, *Nymphoides peltatum (Limnanthemum peltatum)*. The leaves are alternate and the corolla-lobes are not overlapping in bud (valvate), whilst the ovary has only one loculus, with the ovules arranged on the walls. Another distinction is that the vascular bundles of the stem are *collateral* and not *bicollateral* as in *Gentianaceae*.

Buckbean

H.V.A.

Rose Bay, Willow Herb

(CHAMAENERION ANGUSTIFOLIUM)

WHENEVER a pinewood is cut down and left untouched for two or three years it frequently becomes almost completely covered with this lovely flower. It spreads rapidly by its numerous tiny seeds which float away in the wind by means of a tuft of slender white hairs, rather like those of some thistles.

On bombed sites, even in the heart of London, and in other cities and towns, it was one of the first plants to appear after the Second World War. Though one of our most lovely wild flowers, it is to some a noxious weed, particularly to gardeners and nurserymen with peaty soil in which it thrives.

The flowers of the Rose Bay open between 6 and 7 a.m., and the anthers are ready to release their pollen before the stigmas of the same flower are mature, thus preventing self-pollination. Nectar is secreted on the fleshy green top of the ovary, and is protected from rain by the expanded bases of the filaments and the hairs on the style just above them. Insects alight on the stamens, which are prominent while the style is still short, and carry the pollen grains bound together by threads of viscin to an older flower in which the stamens have curved downwards and their place taken by the elongated style with its four broad spreading stigmas, which in turn provide the alighting place

The stems of Rose Bay are usually unbranched, reddish, and up to about 4 ft. high. The leaves are numerous, ascending, narrow like those of a willow, and conspicuously marked by numerous lateral nerves spreading almost at a right angle and looped into a wavy line within the margin. The calyx is closed in bud and has a little hump at the top, the four lobes at length spreading, as also the four purplish red obovate clawed free petals. The stamens are double the number of the petals, and the inferior ovary is four-locular. The fruit is about 2 in. long and splits into four narrow divisions through which the very numerous tiny seeds float away in the wind like the fruits of many of the Daisy family, *Compositae*. A better known name for this plant is *Epilobium angustifolium*.

Rose Bay, Willow Herb

Harebell

(CAMPANULA ROTUNDIFOLIA)

THE Harebell of southern England and Wales is the Bluebell of northern England and of Scotland, celebrated in Scottish ballads. It was also the Bluebell of Elizabethan herbalists, and Lyte, in 1578, described it as " Blew Belles whan their plante beginneth first to spring up . . . have small rounde leaves."

This *Campanula* flowers in late summer and autumn and has a very wide distribution from the Arctic Circle south to the Mediterranean, sometimes at high elevations, and in the northern United States of America and in Canada. Another common name is " Witch's Thimbles," and in the north young children amuse themselves by placing the corolla upside down on the back of the hand, striking it sharply to produce a faint squeak. In France it is called " Clochette," and in Germany " Weisen Busch " or " Milch Glocken," for from the stem when broken there exudes a milk-like sap.

The specific name refers to the rounded toothed leaves at the base of the stem, which soon shrivel up and disappear as the flowers open. The remainder of the leaves are quite narrow and gradually reduced to small bracts. The pendulous flowers vary greatly in size and a white form is found now and then.

Nectar is secreted by a yellow fleshy disk situated on top of the ovary, and it is protected by the broad triangular bases of the filaments. The anthers are at first united in a cone around the stigma. They open inwards and deposit their pollen on the stylar brush in the middle, after which the filaments retract and draw the anthers downwards away from the stigma. Bees effect cross-pollination by brushing against the pollen on the outside of the stigmas and carry it to another and older flower in which the stigmas have already opened out and become receptive. The pollen grains are striking objects under a high power microscope, being whitish, spheroidal, and closely beset with spinose tubercles like the head of an ancient battle-axe.

Harebell

Nettle-leaved Campanula

Nettle-leaved Campanula

(CAMPANULA TRACHELIUM)

ONE of the most interesting features about Campanulas is the way their fruits open—when pendulous, by holes at the actual base, i.e., next to the point of attachment with the stalk, and when erect, at the top just below the calyx-lobes. Through these holes the seeds are shaken out by the wind or when brushed against by passing animals. In this Nettle-leaved Campanula the fruit is pendulous and it opens by three large holes near the base, as in the Harebell.

The Nettle-leaved Campanula grows in woods and flowers from July to September. It is fairly common in some parts of England and Wales and is also found in southern Scotland, but rare in Eire. It is a perennial herb up to about 3 ft. high, with stiff hairs here and there on the ribs of the stem. The lowermost leaves are on long stalks and deeply heart-shaped at the base, but the other leaves gradually become smaller and sessile amongst the flowers. The latter are more or less pendulous, the ovary bristly hairy and 3-locular, and the corolla is blue-purple or rarely white and up to $1\frac{1}{2}$ in. long.

As in the Harebell nectar is secreted in a yellow fleshy disk on top of the ovary and is likewise protected by the broad short filaments of the stamens. The anthers and stigmas behave in the same way as described for the Harebell (page 70), the pollen grains being yellow, spheroidal and covered with spine-like tubercles. If cross-pollination be ineffective, self-pollination may take place by the style-branches recurving, when the stigmas may touch the pollen still held by the outside of the style-branches.

Coltsfoot

Coltsfoot

(TUSSILAGO FARFARA)

COLTSFOOT is often one of the first spring flowers to bloom, and is usually found in great abundance in waste places among rubble, and is sometimes very common on railway embankments, where it helps to bind the loose soil together.

It is a perennial with a slender creeping root-stock emitting numerous upright flowering stems up to about a foot high bearing short, narrow bract-like leaves with woolly hairs and, in addition, minute stalked black glands. These tiny glands are also on the 20 to 25 bracts of the involucre, which are arranged more or less in two rows, the tips tinged with pink.

The ray-flowers are golden yellow, very numerous in three to four rows, each with a linear corolla-lobe (connate petals). These ray-flowers are female and serve to attract bees which search for the nectar secreted at the base of the style of the disk (male) flowers. In doing this they bring about cross-pollination by carrying pollen from one flower-head to another, though self-pollination is possible owing to the closing of the heads at night or during dull or cold weather. Seeds are produced only by the ray-flowers.

After flowering, the real leaves are developed, and they store up food in the root-stock to flower the following spring. Just how many millions of years this has gone on no one can hazard a guess. These leaves are long-stalked and rounded in outline, something like the shape of a colt's foot (hence the common name). They are shortly lobed and toothed, with the main nerves radiating from the base, and are covered below with a soft felt of woolly white hairs. These leaves form the basis of Herb Tobacco, and were much in demand during the Second World War. They were formerly used to staunch wounds and heal sores.

The derivation of the scientific generic name *Tussilago* is from the Latin *tussis,* a cough, from its use as a remedy, and the specific name *farfara* is an ancient name of the white-leaved poplar, the leaves of which bear some resemblance.

Yarrow, Milfoil (pink form)

Yarrow, Milfoil

(ACHILLEA MILLEFOLIUM)

" THE more we are together, the happier we shall be," might very well have been the motto of the Daisy family, *Compositae*, during the course of its long and hazardous evolution. For it would seem that plants of this family discovered long long ago that the best way for them to multiply their kind was to join forces for the production of fertile seeds. If separate, the tiny white or rarely pink flowers of the Yarrow, for example, would never be seen by an insect; joined, however, into a great wide platform, they are a striking object among the grasses, with which they so commonly associate, and provide a convenient landing place for many kinds of insects and small creeping animals which effect cross-pollination.

But most members of the family have " two strings to their bow and can be happy with either," for they are not wholly dependent on insect-visitors to bring about pollination. They can use their own pollen just as well, and the results from either method would seem to be wholly efficient, for the family *Compositae* is by far the largest and most successful group of flowering plants in the world.

Yarrow is very abundant in many kinds of grasslands, particularly on light, dry soil. On lawns it may be regarded as a nuisance, crowding out the more desired grasses. It is very deep-rooting and extremely drought-resistant, continuing fresh and green to the end of dry summers when most other plants have wilted. Each little flower-head has its own tiny envelope of three to four rows of bracts, green up the middle and with brown hairy margins. A striking feature is the reduction of the usually white ray-flowers to five, thus mimicking a simple flower with five petals, a very interesting biological feature.

Ragwort

Ragwort

(SENECIO JACOBAEA)

A PERENNIAL plant with a short thick root-stock which enables it to persist in some fields however much it is trodden on or mown. Though a nuisance to the farmer, it is, nevertheless, a very handsome plant in pastures and on roadsides, sometimes growing in dense masses.

There are several wild kinds of *Senecio* in Britain, the Ragwort standing out by its tall growth, much divided finely toothed leaves, and the often darker coloured tips of the smaller bracts around the flower-head. The achenes or " seed " of the ray (outer) flowers are smooth and without hairs, and those of the disk (inner) flowers covered with short hairs.

A relation of the Ragwort is the common Groundsel (*Senecio vulgaris*), a weed in gardens and cultivated fields, but also a useful bird food, whilst in the Mountains of the Moon in East Africa there are giant species with single stems up to 15 ft. high and with huge broad leaves, which give a very quaint and weird aspect to the landscape.

Sheep may eat Ragwort in a young state with impunity, but later it becomes unpalatable and distinctly poisonous, especially to cattle. The effects of eating it are not always immediately apparent, small quantities of the plant taken repeatedly depositing the poison in the system until sufficient is present to cause serious illness, which may end fatally. In Canada Ragwort is the cause of the *Pictou* cattle disease, or cirrhosis of the liver, and sheep in New Zealand are affected in the same way after eating it. In South Africa a closely related native species is equally poisonous.

Creeping Thistle

Creeping Thistle

(CIRSIUM ARVENSE)

THE common name of this thistle is rather unfortunate, the character referring to the creeping root-stock and not to the general habit, which is very much erect. It is especially abundant in cultivated and waste places and is probably the commonest weed pest of agriculture.

The stems of this troublesome species appear annually from the creeping rhizome, and if mown at an early stage the plants can in time be much weakened and eradicated. The stems are closely ribbed and often prickly with the decurrent bases of the sessile leaves. These are oblanceolate in outline but deeply and undulately lobed and margined by numerous very sharp prickles varying much in length. The young leaves are woolly but soon become glabrous or nearly so.

The flower-heads vary from being nearly sessile in a cluster-like corymb to quite long-pedunculate. They are unisexual, the males on one plant, the females on another. The male heads are nearly globose with very projecting rose-purple or rarely white flowers and very conspicuous anthers, the females narrower and with longer bracts but shorter flowers with conspicuous stigmas. The pappus in the females soon becomes a prominent feature and consists of long silky hairs which are markedly feathery, i.e., with long side hairs. The achenes are quite smooth and blackish.

It is due to the presence of a large number of male plants that leads farmers to think that the seeds of the Creeping Thistle do not germinate.

Greater Fleabane

(PULICARIA DYSENTERICA)

GREATER FLEABANE is sometimes very plentiful on wet grasslands, especially those with heavy clay soil. To reduce it or get rid of it, regular cutting is recommended, as it is a perennial with a creeping root-stock ; draining the land is also effective. It flowers in late summer and autumn, and is in some places very common by roadsides, where it often makes quite a show of colour.

This plant is very easy to recognize merely by its leaves, which are sessile on the stem and arrow-shaped at the base. They are well shown in Miss Abbott's lovely painting. The densely leafy stems are ribbed, and whitish with woolly hairs, like the undersurface of the leaves. The bracts of the involucre are numerous and very narrow with thread-like tips. The flower-heads are not more than $1\frac{1}{2}$ in. in diameter, but they contain as many as 600 disk-flowers in the middle, and upwards of 100 yellow ray-flowers on the margin— a veritable *multum in parvo !*

The tiny disk-flowers are perfect, i.e., they are bisexual, having both stamens and pistil, but the ray-flowers are of one sex, female, without any stamens, as in most other members of the Daisy family *(Compositae)*. The anthers of the disk-flowers are united into a tube around the style. The latter brushes out the pollen which is largely held by the upper triangular sterile portions of the anthers. After this occurs the style-arms spread out and become receptive to pollen from other flowers previously visited by an insect.

H.V A

Greater Fleabane

Greater Knapweed

(CENTAUREA SCABIOSA)

GREATER KNAPWEED is so-called because it is taller and has larger and more showy flower-heads than its much more common relative, the Lesser Knapweed or Hardheads as it is often called *(Centaurea nigra).*

It is a perennial with a thick underground woody root-stock from which the hard ribbed rather woolly-pubescent stems grow up year after year. It is, therefore, well worth a place in the herbaceous border in the garden. The lowermost leaves have a slender stalk, but those higher up are sessile, and all are deeply pinnately lobed. Surrounding the flowers are several rows (8-10) of bracts, gradually becoming larger from below upwards, and all of them have their black margins fringed with bristles like a comb, and with green up the middle.

The flowers around the margin of the head are larger and stick out from those in the middle. They serve to render the flower-head conspicuous to insects, and they mimic the ray-flowers of other members of the family. They are, however, quite sterile and have no nectar, such as is secreted in the disk flowers. The filaments of the darker coloured disk-flowers are irritable, and when touched by an insect bend and pull down the anther-cylinder, when the ring of hairs at the base of the style-arms, characteristic of this group of *Compositae*, brushes out the pollen.

Greater Knapweed is generally distributed in England and Wales, being more common in chalky districts, but it extends a very short way into Scotland, and is local and rare in Eire. Sometimes, by the wayside in the chalk downs it forms a little flower-garden of its own.

Centaurea is a very large genus with numerous species in the Mediterranean and Caucasus regions, and there are many beautiful species in cultivation in British gardens.

Greater Knapweed

Mouse-Ear Hawkweed

(HIERACIUM PILOSELLA)

IF examined in detail with a fairly strong lens this plant will be found to be full of botanical interest. It is one of the most easily recognized species of this large and difficult genus, composed of innumerable so-called species. Its common English name is derived from the fancied resemblance of the hairy tips of the leaves to a mouse's ear. Syme, *English Botany*, says that in Gloucestershire and probably elsewhere in the south, a beautiful gold and green beetle haunts this flower, loving to

" Sit in the centre, and enjoy a bright day "

and at certain angles of view is scarcely distinguishable by reason of its lustre.

The spreading tufts of radical leaves arise from a perennial root-stock, with creeping offshoots bearing smaller, narrow, spoon-shaped leaves, rather densely clothed with long slender and very short white hairs. The leaves are green above and loosely covered with long stiff bulbous-based hairs, woolly-tomentose below with white star-shaped hairs. The stalk of the flower-head and the bracts surrounding the latter are also covered by an under-layer of minute star-shaped hairs as well as stiff blackish often gland-tipped hairs.

Mouse-Ear Hawkweed

Bindweed

(CONVOLVULUS ARVENSIS)

IT is unfortunate that such a lovely flower is also a troublesome weed, which, when once established, is very difficult to eradicate from the garden or field. This is due to its extensive root-system, which can penetrate the soil to a great depth. The stems are prostrate or twine spirally up other plants which they tend to strangle.

The leaves are more or less triangular or broadly arrow-shaped, and the lovely delicate flowers are usually in pairs on axillary stalks, only one of each pair being open at the same time. In bud the corolla-lobes are spirally twisted and spread out almost horizontally from the very short tube. The flowers are fragrant and close up during bad weather and at night. They last only one day. The corolla is either reddish with five white streaks lengthwise, or entirely white (var. *hololeucus*) ; the base is yellow.

Nectar is secreted by the orange-yellow base of the ovary and covered by the broadened lower ends of the filaments, leaving only five narrow nectar-passages. As the stamens surround the style and their anthers dehisce outwards, the latter must be touched by any large insect sucking the nectar which carries the pollen to the stigmas of another flower.

Where the filaments touch they are closely beset with small stiff projections, preventing the passage of an insect's proboscis, which must be inserted into one of the five narrow passages in order to reach the nectar. Should insect-visits fail, automatic self-pollination may take place towards the end of flowering when the pedicels bend down and the corolla drops, so that pollen falls on the stigma.

Bindweed

Bird's-eye, Germander Speedwell

Bird's-eye, Germander Speedwell
(VERONICA CHAMAEDRYS)

THIS lovely little plant flowers in spring and early summer, growing in partial shade on hedge-banks, and is a great favourite with children. The French name for it is *Véronique Petit Chêne* and the German, *Germander Ehrenpreis*.

The flowers close up at night and then show only the pearly side of the bright-blue corolla, looking, as Syme said of it, " as though its tiny stalk bore a pearl rather than a flower." Even Ebenezer Elliott (1781-1849), known as the corn-law rhymer, extolled its charms :

" Blue eye-bright! Loveliest flower of all that grow
   In flower-loved England! Flower whose hedge-side gaze
   Is like an infant's! "

Although so small a plant it is a perennial and appears in the same spots year after year. It may be recognised at once among the 18 or so native British species especially by the two opposite lines of whitish hairs on the stem, in the same plane as the leaves (not hairy all around), the flowers in slender racemes from the axils of the upper leaves, the common stalk being covered all around with fine hairs. The four-lobed corolla is particularly beautiful when seen through a lens, deep sky-blue fading to mauve inside, marked with deeper blue lines, and with a white " eye," the mouth of the very short tube guarded with erect bristly hairs on the lower side ; the filaments and anthers of the only two stamens as well as the style also blue.

The nectar, for which insects visit the flower, is secreted by a fleshy disk below the ovary, and is protected from marauders by the hairs in the corolla-tube mentioned above. The flowers open between nine and ten o'clock in the morning, closing again in the evening from five to six (Greenwich time). The two stamens spread away from the middle of the flower and the style is directed obliquely downwards. Thus, an insect alighting on the lower corolla-lobe, the most convenient platform, must first touch the stigma with its ventral surface, depositing pollen on it from flowers previously visited. Automatic self-pollination takes place when the flowers remain closed during inclement weather.

Bittersweet, Woody Nightshade

Bittersweet, Woody Nightshade

(SOLANUM DULCAMARA)

BITTERSWEET is so-called because the stem at first tastes bitter and then sweetish. The whole plant, however, is poisonous in all parts and contains the alkaloid *solanine*. Although farm animals rarely touch it, they may occasionally do so when eating other leaves from hedges over which it climbs, especially those alongside wet ditches and brooks. Poisoning in human beings has usually been confined to children, who may be tempted to eat the attractive red berries.

The plant is a perennial herb, woody at the base, with an underground root-stock and straggly stems several feet long with alternate ovate simple or deeply three-lobed leaves. The flowers are very similar to those of the potato and arranged in small panicles, the common stalk of which is placed opposite to and not in the axil of a leaf ; corolla blue, marked with violet veins, with a very short tube and five spreading lobes which do not overlap in bud (valvate) ; anthers standing up in a cone around the style, each opening by two pores at the top ; ovary two-locular with several ovules in each chamber attached to the central axis ; fruit ovoid or globular, red.

The blossoms of Bittersweet are only slightly fragrant. Around the base of the stamens the concave receptacle is blue-black and shines as if it were covered with a thin layer of fluid. The receptacle is surrounded by projections, green and white margins, and situated in pairs at the bases of the corolla-lobes. Flies visit these projections and then go to the stigma and the tips of the pollen-covered anthers, bringing about cross-pollination when they visit other flowers.

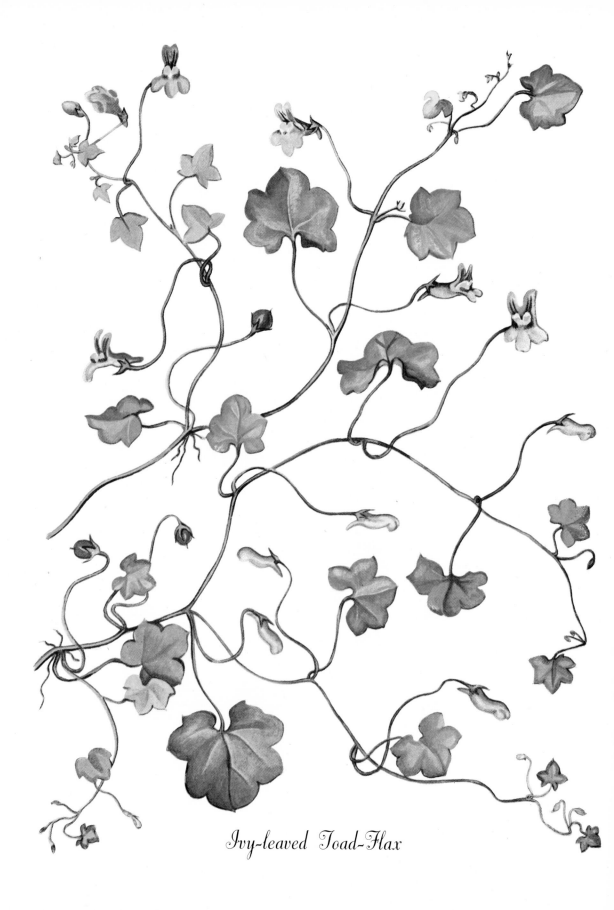

Ivy-leaved Toad-Flax

Ivy-leaved Toad-Flax

(LINARIA CYMBALARIA)

ONLY a very few species of British wild flowers are adapted to grow on rocks and old walls. The Ivy-leaved Toad Flax is one of these. It is a small succulent trailing perennial herb with slender thread-like stems rooting at the lower nodes.

The leaves are long-stalked with a kidney-shaped blade broadly and shortly five-lobed, the lobes slightly pointed and often tinged with purple; the main nerves radiate from the point of attachment of the leaf-stalk.

The flowers are small, but very lovely and solitary in the leaf-axils on slender stalks. They are two-lipped (personate) and adapted to the visits of humble bees. The short tubular corolla is lilac, the tube streaked with crimson-purple, and the two humps on the lower lip, which are tinged with orange, serve to close up the tube, in the spur of which is stored the nectar. On the lower side of the tube the nectar is protected by a dense carpet of stiff inwardly directed hairs.

There are only four stamens, two longer and two shorter, and the stalks of the longer stamens are hairy at the base. The tiny ovary is two-locular with numerous ovules attached to the dividing wall, and the fruit is a rounded capsule containing several warted seeds.

This interesting little plant flowers from the late spring until the autumn and is remarkably resistant to very dry conditions and long periods of drought. Bees in searching for the nectar alight on the lower lip and by their weight are able to press it down and gain access to it. A most interesting biological feature is that, after fertilization takes place, the flower-stalks curve towards darker crevices in the wall, in which the seeds are deposited when the fruit ripens and bursts.

Yellow Toad-Flax

Yellow Toad-Flax

(LINARIA VULGARIS)

THE genus *Linaria* belongs to the Scrophularia family, *Scrophularia-ceae*, which is very well represented in the British flora, other familiar examples being the Foxglove and Mullein, as well as the Snap-dragons in our gardens. *Linaria* is very closely related to the Snapdragon, differing mainly in having a long-spurred corolla.

Yellow Toad-flax is a perennial with a short creeping root-stock, often quite common by roadsides, in hedges, and on the margins of fields. The stems are erect and up to as much as 3 ft. high, rounded, shining green, without any hairs ; leaves alternate, linear, bright green above, paler below ; flowers crowded into a leafy raceme with a bunch of young leaves at the top. The corolla is pale yellow and very tightly two-lipped, with the bulging portion of the lower lip bright orange and densely hairy inside ; tube prolonged into a sharp-pointed spur up to $\frac{3}{4}$ in. long. There are four stamens in unequal pairs and hidden beneath the lower lip, with the stigma between them.

Nectar is secreted at the base of the ovary and overflows into the spur which it fills for a short distance. The length of the spur prevents short-tongued bees from reaching the nectar, while the tightly closed lips exclude flies, lepidoptera and beetles. Only long-tongued bees can legitimately suck the nectar and effect cross-pollination. They press down the lower lip and creep into the corolla. In doing so they brush the dorsal side of their bodies against the simultaneously mature anthers and stigma and bring about cross-pollination when they visit another flower. Sometimes a honey-bee makes a short cut by biting a hole in the spur and stealing the nectar.

H.V.A.

Monkey Flower

Monkey Flower

(MIMULUS GUTTATUS)

A STUDENT of our wild flowers may well be puzzled when he finds the Monkey Flower for the first time, for it appears to be quite at home and truly native amongst the herbage in or near brooks and by the sides of mountain streams. I well remember the first time I found a lovely patch by the side of a burn above Fort William in Scotland, and how keen I was to get back to the Kew Herbarium to find out its name.

The native home of the Monkey Flower is, however, North America, and it has escaped from gardens and become naturalized in many places in Britain. It is an erect herb up to about $1\frac{1}{2}$ ft. high with an angular hollow stem, the basal leaves broadly stalked and rounded, with coarse unequal teeth ; main nerves several and parallel with the margin ; upper leaves opposite and sessile, rounded and sharply toothed, about 1 in. long and broad ; flowers solitary in the axils of the upper leaves, the corolla in bud resembling a boat with the keel uppermost ; calyx five-angled and shortly lobed, pale green ; corolla rich yellow, two-lipped, with bright reddish spots on the lower lip and inside the tube, the lower lip with numerous bristly yellow hairs on the hump.

There are four stamens, two longer, with their anthers just below the broad stigma, and two shorter. The ovary is shortly stalked (stipitate), two-locular, with numerous ovules. The fruit is a capsule opening by two valves into the loculi.

The stigma is irritable, and bees first touch the lower lobe which covers the anthers of the two longer stamens, and they dust it with pollen if they have previously visited another flower. The nectar which they seek is secreted at the base of the ovary.

Foxglove

(DIGITALIS PURPUREA)

ANOTHER and very significant name for this lovely flower, besides Foxglove, is "Dead Man's Bells." For it has been recognized as poisonous for centuries. All parts have this property, especially the seeds, and the dried leaves are listed in the British Pharmacopaeia as being used in medicine for heart trouble. The leaves are less active after the flowering period, however, but they may prove dangerous if mixed with hay and fed to stock, cases of death having been recorded.

The plant is a biennial, i.e., it produces a seedling one year which flowers and seeds the next and then dies. A vast number of seeds are produced by one plant. It is one of the most handsome and conspicuous of our wild flowers and rivals the Rose Bay, which it also resembles in its habit, of suddenly appearing in great numbers in open spaces in woods which have been recently cleared or burnt over. It is not at all tolerant of chalky soil.

The lowermost leaves of the Foxglove are long-stalked, the stalks being winged by the decurrent leaf-blade. They are sometimes up to a foot or more in length and finely toothed on the margins, the surface being crinkly with the coarsely netted veins which are softly downy below. The upper leaves gradually diminish into bracts and are spirally arranged, though the flowers all fall to one side of the main axis.

The calyx is deeply five-lobed, the fifth lobe next to the main axis being smaller than the others. The ovary is two-locular and is covered by minute gland-tipped hairs. The capsule contains very small minutely honeycombed seeds.

An insect alighting on the oblique mouth of the corolla meets with a veritable wonderland of colour inside the tube which is beautifully mottled with crimson spots on a whitish background. It is retarded in its entry, however, by a number of long bristle-like white hairs which cause it to press up against the four anthers arched on the upper side of the tube. These shed their pollen on the insect's back, by which it is carried to the stigma of another and older flower.

Foxglove

Meadow Crane's-bill

(GERANIUM PRATENSE)

IN many parts of Britain the grassy waysides, meadows and hay fields are brightened from June to August, but especially during July, with masses of this most lovely of our native species of *Geranium*. This, by the way, is a different genus from the bedding "Geranium" of our gardens and window-boxes. The latter is a *Pelargonium,* of which there are very many different kinds in the Union of South Africa. The difference is that in *Geranium* the flowers have no spur, whilst in *Pelargonium* there is a spur, but it is concealed within the flower-stalk and is easily detected by cutting a cross-section of the latter.

Meadow Crane's-bill is a perennial favouring moist places, some-times in permanent hayfields, and its seeds have been scheduled as injurious to stock. In rich soil it grows to as much as 4 ft. in height. The basal leaves are rounded and deeply lobulate and coarsely toothed, hairy on the strong nerves below. The stem-leaves are opposite with a pair of stipules fringed with hairs between each stalk. The upper parts of the stem and the flower-stalks are covered with spreading gland-tipped hairs which protect the flowers from creeping insects which would otherwise steal the nectar.

The flowers are mostly in pairs on long peduncles, with crimson bracts at the base of the stalks. The five sepals are beaked at the apex, and five-nerved, and the five deep-violet-blue petals are nearly 1 in. long and broad, with crimson nerves.

The ten stamens at first lie on the petals but become erect when the anthers open and pass to the middle of the flower. As soon as the pollen is shed they bend back again and the stigmas become receptive to pollen transferred by insects from previously visited flowers. Nectar is secreted at the outside of the base of the five inner stamens.

Meadow Crane's-bill

Borage

(BORAGO OFFICINALIS

THIS may well be called the " Borage of the Borages," for it is the *type species* of the genus *Borago*, which is itself the *type genus* of the family *Boraginaceae!*

Borage has for a long time been cultivated in gardens in this country and has become naturalized in many places, especially in waste ground near houses, where it flowers most of the summer. Its native habitat is the eastern Mediterranean. It is commonly grown in kitchen gardens both for its uses as a herb and for the sake of its flowers, being an excellent bee plant. Formerly, the young tips of Borage were boiled as a pot herb, and the young leaves were considered to be good in salads, being reputed " to exhilarate and make the mind glad and drive away sorrow." The leaves eaten raw were supposed to purify the blood after sickness.

The plant is an annual or biennial herb covered all over with bristle-like one-celled hairs. The larger leaves have a broad stalk, the upper ones becoming sessile, the lovely blue or white flowers hanging in loose forked terminal cymes also densely clothed with long white hairs.

The corolla is expanded to form a nearly flat surface, from the centre of which the black cone of anthers projects. The latter open inwards by a pore-like slit, and they have on the back a purple horn-like appendage about half as long as the anther itself.

The powdery pollen falls into the tip of the cone and surrounds the stigma, but as the latter is still immature automatic self-pollination is excluded. When an insect visits a flower it clings to the cone of anthers and becomes dusted with the pollen which it carries away to another and older flower in which the stigma has become receptive, thus bringing about cross-pollination.

H.V.A.

Borage

Hedge Stachys

(STACHYS SYLVATICA)

BEFORE it flowers this plant may easily be mistaken for the common stinging nettle, which it greatly resembles in its square stems and large opposite heart-shaped leaves. But there are no stinging hairs as in the nettle.

The stem is hollow and covered, especially on the angles, with spreading or downwardly directed bulbous-based hairs. The leaf-stalks are connected at the base by a bristly hairy rim. It blooms from July onwards in hedges and woods, the flowers being arranged in whorls of about six to ten, the upper ones becoming more crowded and the leaves reduced to bracts. The calyx is equally five-lobed, the lobes triangular, acute, and glandular-hairy outside. The corolla is two-lipped, the lower lip being beautifully mottled like the petals of an Orchis, the mottling serving as a nectar-guide to insects.

The upper lip of the corolla not only shelters the anthers and stigma in bad weather, but also protects the nectar from rain. The nectar is secreted by the base of the ovary and is stored in the smooth basal part of the corolla-tube. A circle of hairs just above the nectar keeps away unwelcome visitors, such as flies, which would otherwise steal the nectar without effecting cross-pollination. At first the tip of the style is situated behind the anthers, which open downwards. Later on it bends down under the anthers, at the same time opening its branches widely. When visited by a humble-bee, therefore, cross-pollination is ensured, the stigma of older flowers being dusted by pollen from younger ones. The flowers are also frequently perforated by short-tongued humble-bees.

The four fruitlets when half-ripe are green, with a purplish tip, and are smooth and brightly shining.

Hedge Stachys

Bugle

Bugle
(AJUGA REPTANS)

THE common Bugle is a lovely wild flower which follows the Primrose in fields and grassy open spaces in woods, sometimes in deep shade. Its root-stock produces numerous elongated runner-like shoots (stolons) by which it spreads and multiplies.

The flowers are borne in tiers in the axils of the opposite obovate three- to five-nerved leaves, the uppermost forming a slightly interrupted spike-like inflorescence. The stems, like those of the Bird's Eye, have lines of hairs below the leaves between the purple angles. The blue or rarely pink corolla is interesting and distinctive because it has only one lip, which is divided into three lobes, the middle lobe being broadest and slightly notched. This lip is marked with brighter lines which serve as guides to insects seeking the nectar which is secreted by a thick yellow gland situated in front of the ovary and discharged into the pouch-like base of the corolla-tube.

As there is little or no upper lip to the corolla to cover the anthers and stigma, as in most other members of the family *Labiatae*, its absence is compensated for by the leafy bracts of the flowers immediately above, which protect them from rain. Humble-bees effect cross-pollination, and self-pollination may also take place.

The young flower-buds of this species are well worth examining under a hand-lens for they are whiskered like a sea-lion. The ovary is deeply lobed into four parts which in fruit develop into separate nutlets, finely reticulate with a large lateral scar at the base by which they were attached to the floral axis.

Flowering Rush

Flowering Rush

(BUTOMUS UMBELLATUS)

THE Flowering Rush belongs to a very primitive group of Mono-cotyledons (plants with only one seed-leaf) characterized by having *free carpels*, just as in the buttercup family. Indeed, they seem to be fairly closely related. A very ancient feature of the carpels is that the ovules are scattered over their inside walls and not confined to placentas as, for example, in the Lily family *(Liliaceae)*. The arrangement of the flowers (the inflorescence), however, is considerably advanced and very similar to that of the Amaryllis family, in which the ovary is mostly *inferior*.

Butomus is one of the most stately and elegant of our native aquatics, though it is by no means common. Syme (*British Plants*) quotes :—

" Her rosy umbels rears the Flowering Rush,
  While with reflected charms the waters blush."

The plant is a perennial with a thick, horizontally creeping root-stock; the stem and leaves are filled with lax spongy tissue; leaves long and narrow, closely lined lengthwise by slender nerves and with a distinct thicker midrib; the flowering stem itself is leafless and up to 4 ft. high, bearing at the top and well away from the water an umbel of 20 to 30 pretty pink flowers surrounded by an involucre of three large triangular bracts, with a few smaller bracts among the flower-stalks; the six sepals and petals are all alike and pale pink like petals, overlapping in bud. The nine anthers are at first elongated, but become rounded when open, and there are six free carpels, both anthers and carpels being dark red.

Nectar is abundantly secreted on the carpels themselves, and there is always a large drop collected in the cleft between adjacent members. The six outermost stamens open first and their filaments bend outwards. When these have withered the anthers of the three inner stamens open and release their pollen.

H.V.A.

Bog Asphodel

Bog Asphodel

(NARTHECIUM OSSIFRAGUM)

THE botanical name *Narthecium* is derived from the Greek *narthecion*, a chest or box for holding ointments, ironically given to this plant because it was formerly supposed to break the bones of sheep feeding on it. The second name *ossifragum* also means bone-breaker, which further emphasises its supposed qualities. The plant is regarded as poisonous, especially to cows, and it is on record that a cat died after drinking milk from an affected cow.

The most striking features of this pretty little species, which grows in bogs and wet moors in acid soil, are the densely hairy filaments of the stamens and the very remarkable seeds. The latter have a small ellipsoid central body with a long tail at each end. Certain rhododendrons found in Malaya, which grow on trees and bare rocks (epiphytes), have very similar seeds.

Bog Asphodel is a perennial with a short, creeping root-stock ; stem up to about 1 ft. high, leafy at the base, the leaves arranged in two opposite rows, like those of an *Iris*, and strongly ribbed. The flowers are fragrant, with a scent like that of an orchid, *Platanthera bifolia*, according to Knuth. The sepals are similar to the petals, bright yellow, but green on the back ; stamens six, the filaments, as noted above, densely covered with yellow woolly hairs ; anthers strikingly red ; fruit a capsule splitting from the top into three parts ; seeds as described above.

Though the flowers are fragrant they secrete no nectar and soon after they open the anthers and stigma mature at the same time. But the stamens soon diverge widely from the stigma, which prevents self-pollination. Cross-pollination takes place through insects which visit the flowers to collect the pollen.

The genus *Narthecium* is a very small one of three or four species, very like each other, and widely distributed around the north temperate zone.

Fritillary,
Snake's Head

Fritillary, Snake's Head

(FRITILLARIA MELEAGRIS)

THIS lovely flower is found in moist meadows only in the southern counties of England, but is rarely seen except by those who are fortunate to know where it grows. It has always been one of the sights early in the year in the Iffley Fields at Oxford. In some localities it covers acres of ground and is commonly known as the Snake's Head Lily.

The specific name refers to the chequered appearance of the flowers, which is not unlike that of a chess-board. In Germany it is called Schachblume (Chess-flower) and Kukuksei (Cuckoo's Egg), on account of its shape, size, and markings. The species has a wide distribution as far east as the Caucasus mountains.

It is a herb with a bulbous base, the bulbs sometimes clustered ; scales few and thick ; stem single, bearing a few scattered alternate leaves, these linear, blunt and curved at the apex, closely and faintly nerved ; flowers usually single, drooping, composed of six free broad segments tessellated with dull purple, rarely white or yellowish ; stamens inserted at the base of the perianth ; anthers very long, quite $\frac{1}{2}$ in., yellow ; ovary long and triangular, three-locular ; style with three stigmas ; ovules numerous ; fruit an erect capsule, with three valves, the valves hairy on the margins.

The inner parts of the flower are protected from rain by its pendulous position and the close arrangement of the perianth-segments. Nectar is secreted in a groove on the inside of each of these segments, beginning well above the base and continued almost to its tip. The flower is described as protogynous, i.e., the stigmas are receptive before the anthers release their pollen. The flowering period lasts about five days and if cross-pollination has not taken place, self-pollination is probable. One of the six stamens then usually elongates, so that its anther reaches the level of the still receptive stigma, and sheds its pollen, a very interesting and remarkable phenomenon.

Bluebell

Bluebell

(SCILLA NONSCRIPTA)

ALTHOUGH now such a well-known and popular flower, the Bluebell is only once mentioned by Shakespeare, but not under that name.

> "Thou shalt not lack
> The flower that's like thy face, pale Primrose, nor
> The asured Harebell, like thy veins"
>
> *Cymbeline* iv. 2. 220.

The Harebell of Shakespeare was undoubtedly the Bluebell or Wild Hyacinth, and not the real Harebell, *Campanula rotundifolia,* which is the Bluebell of northern England and of Scotland (*see* page 70).

The bulb of the Bluebell is white and is filled with juice by the time the leaves die down in early summer and stored up until the next spring. The narrow strap-shaped leaves are up to 1 ft. long and widely V-shaped. The flowering stem is leafless and normally up to about 1 ft. in height, very juicy, smooth and shining. At the base of each individual flower-stalk is a pair of unequal-sized narrow bluish-purple bracts. There are six sky-blue (rarely white) perianth-segments, each with a stamen opposite to it, three of the stamens being longer and three shorter; anthers white and rather large. The ovary is three-locular, with two rows of ovules arranged on the central axis, and the fruit is a capsule full of black seeds.

Nectar is exposed or half-concealed and is secreted by the septal glands of the ovary and stored between the latter and the bases of the filaments.

Kew Gardens is justly famed for its lovely stretches of Bluebells, in the Queen's Cottage grounds, and they are usually at their best about the first week in May. Large areas are covered with this beautiful flower, and the sea of colour beneath the beech and birch trees just breaking into leaf is worth travelling a long way to see. Many of the woods in the counties around London are likewise full of Bluebells.

The species is found in a wild state only in the western part of Europe, extending along the Mediterranean as far as Italy.

Lady's Slipper

(CYPRIPEDIUM CALCEOLUS)

LADY'S SLIPPER is probably our loveliest and rarest native orchid. More than 100 years ago botanists prophesied that owing to people collecting it to grow in their gardens it was liable to be soon exterminated as a wild flower. That prophesy was nearly fulfilled, and its distribution was soon confined to a few localities. Fortunately, in the few places where it still grows in one of our northern counties it is now well protected in private woods. Formerly, it was found in limestone soil in oak-hazel woods in Westmorland, Yorkshire and Durham.

Although so rare in Britain, Lady's Slipper grows wild right across Europe and Asia as far as the island of Saghalien, to the north of Japan. In central Europe it is found in woods at a much higher altitude than in Britain, from 5,000-7,000 ft. in Switzerland and the Tirol. Another species is found in Canada and the United States, called *Cypripedium parviflorum*, which is so similar as to be scarcely distinguishable, though it favours quite different soil, being found in peat bogs or moist woods in rather rich soil.

Orchids are classified into two groups or subfamilies, the *Diandreae*, with two stamens, and the *Monandreae*, with only one stamen. Lady's Slipper is the only representative of the first group found wild in Britain, all the others belonging to the second group. The first group, with two stamens, is evidently the more primitive, and in the genus *Cypripedium* the pollen grains are not joined together into pollen masses (pollinia). In this feature it shows a distant relationship with the Lily and Iris families.

Pollination is effected by small insects which creep into the slipper, from which they eventually escape, carrying away in the process some of the sticky pollen to another flower, and effecting cross-pollination. For details of this and other British orchids the reader should consult V. S. Summerhayes's excellent book, one of Collins's New Naturalist Series, entitled *Wild Orchids of Britain* (1951).

H.N.A.

Lady's Slipper

Bee Orchid

(OPHRYS APIFERA)

SOME things stand out more prominently than others in our journey through life. Few people may be able to remember the thrilling moment when they first took a few tottering steps from their mother's knee. I cannot, I fear, recall my own emancipation from the creeping stage. But I do remember most vividly many other thrilling incidents in my life ; the first time I balanced myself unaided on a penny-farthing bicycle ; the end of my first week's wages ; the first kiss of my first love ; the first ride on a motor bicycle ; the pull of my first salmon at the end of the line ; and many other first experiences, both pleasant and unpleasant.

One of the greatest thrills when plant collecting, as a young botanist, was when I found, for the first time, a specimen of a Bee Orchid on the slopes of Box Hill, in Surrey ; and it still ranks high in my list of botanical remembrances, which have been many and varied during more than half a century. I have looked for it in the same place many times since ; sometimes it was still there, often it was not to be found, which is a characteristic of this remarkable orchid.

Bee Orchid flowers from June to July and ranges from Britain, through Holland and north-west Germany to the Mediterranean region, North Africa, Asia Minor, and the Caucasus mountains. It is usually found in chalky soils in England, Wales and Eire, but is very rare in Scotland.

The root-system consists of ovoid or globose tubers, and there is a rosette of a few rather broadish grey-green leaves which are carried on from the previous autumn and remain green all the winter. The spike bears up to about seven rather widely spaced flowers with spreading sepals, varying from pale pink to bright violet-rose with green veins rarely white ; petals green or brown ; lip bag-like, reddish or purplish brown with a lovely soft velvety surface marked with paler lines and blotches. It is this lip which bears such a striking resemblance to the body of a bee and which is mistaken for a female by a male member of the same species of insect.

Bee Orchid

H.V.A.

Yellow Iris

(IRIS PSEUDACORUS)

YELLOW IRIS is one of the most handsome of our wild flowers and well worth growing in a bog garden, being quite as beautiful as many exotic kinds. Though the flowers secrete nectar which attracts insects, they are quite without scent. It grows in wet places and by the side of water courses, and extends eastwards far into Russia and south into northern Africa.

In France this Iris is supposed to have furnished the heralds with the device called " Fleur-de-lys," the national bearings adopted by Louis VII, and derived from the river Lys, on the borders of Flanders, on the banks of which it was particularly abundant.

Characteristics are the sharp-edged sword-like leaves, and the three stamens which are hidden by the large fringed petal-like stigmas. The bright-yellow flowers are borne at the top of the stem and appear one at a time from a sheathing bract. The outer perianth-segments are recurved, broad, with a deeper band of colour across the middle, the inner segments being erect, narrow, and very much smaller than the outer; the ovary is below the perianth (inferior), three-locular, and with numerous ovules attached to the central axis. The petal-like stigmas alternate with the inner perianth-segments and are split into two parts at the top, with a short scale-like appendage inside. Petal-like stigmas are very rare. The seeds are pale green or brown and not so attractive as the second native species, *Iris foetidissima*, with orange or scarlet seeds, much less common and mostly found in our southern counties.

Nectar is secreted by the base of the perianth and stored in the tube between this and the style. Insect visitors creep forward on the platform provided by the broad outer segments and under the branched style, dusting the latter with pollen brought from another flower and effecting cross-pollination. An insect needs a proboscis 7 mm. long in order to reach the nectar and 15 mm. long to suck it all out.

Yellow Iris

Lords and Ladies, Cuckoo Pint

(ARUM MACULATUM)

IN the reign of Queen Elizabeth I this plant was called Starchwort, and was used for stiffening the ruffs and frills so fashionable during that period.

Gerrard says of it in his Herball :—

" The most pure and white starch is made of the roots of the Cuckoo Pint, but most hurtful for the hand of the laundresse that hath the handling of it ; for it chappeth, blistereth, and maketh the hands rough and rugged, and withall smarting."

All parts of this plant are harmful, and children who have eaten the attractive looking red berries have been fatally poisoned. The white tuber-like corms are full of starch and when ground to a pulp and powdered were formerly known as Portland Arrowroot.

Arum maculatum starts to grow early in March, completing its active vegetative and flowering period by the end of May, before the canopy of deciduous foliage is fully formed. From then until late summer its fruits become more and more conspicuous. The leaves are long-stalked, more or less triangular, broadly arrow-shaped at the base, and dark, shining green often spotted with purple or streaked with lighter bands of colour.

The reproductive part is not just a simple flower, but is a highly complicated collection of flowers (*inflorescence*). These flowers are enclosed by a large green and purple sheath (known as the *spathe* and really a modified leaf). The floral axis (*spadix*) ends at the top in a large stigma-like, barren, bright purple portion, and below this are borne the flowers, which are of one sex, the upper cluster being male and crowded into a dense mass, each male flower consisting of a single stamen. The lowermost flowers are female, each composed of a single carpel. Above each cluster are a few abortive flowers which are reduced to hair-like structures, those above the male being longer and directed downwards. Small insects creep into the spathe, attracted by the rather disagreeable urinous smell, and are trapped for a time by the downwardly directed hairs, and become dusted with the pollen, which, when they are released, they carry to the stigmas of another collection of female flowers on another plant, bringing about cross-pollination.

Lords and Ladies, Cuckoo Pint

Printed by
EDSON (PRINTERS) LTD.
Hunters Lane, Leavesden
Watford, Herts.